CW00670716

CHRISTMAS
ON THE FARM

Also by Adam Henson from Sphere:

Two for Joy:

The Untold Ways to Enjoy the Countryside

ADAM HENSON

CHRISTMAS ON THE FARM

WINTRY TALES FROM A LIFE SPENT WORKING WITH ANIMALS

WITH JEAN RITCHIE

SPHERE

SPHERE

First published in Great Britain in 2023 by Sphere

1 3 5 7 9 10 8 6 4 2

Copyright © Henson and Andrews Limited 2023

The moral right of the author has been asserted.

*All characters and events in this publication, other than those
clearly in the public domain, are fictitious and any resemblance
to real persons, living or dead, is purely coincidental.*

All rights reserved.
No part of this publication may be reproduced, stored in a
retrieval system, or transmitted, in any form or by any means, without
the prior permission in writing of the publisher, nor be otherwise circulated
in any form of binding or cover other than that in which it is published
and without a similar condition including this condition being
imposed on the subsequent purchaser.

A CIP catalogue record for this book is available from the British Library.

Hardback ISBN 978-1-4087-2739-3

Typeset in Sabon by M Rules
Printed and bound in Great Britain by Clays Ltd, Elcograph, s.P.a.

Lines from 'The Horse' by Ronald Duncan are reproduced
by kind permission of the Estate of Ronald Duncan

Holly motif courtesy Shutterstock

Papers used by Sphere are from well-managed forests
and other responsible sources.

Sphere
An imprint of
Little, Brown Book Group
Carmelite House
50 Victoria Embankment
London EC4Y 0DZ

An Hachette UK Company
www.hachette.co.uk

www.littlebrown.co.uk

I'd like to dedicate this book to my three loving sisters, Libby, Lolo and Becca, who shared so many exciting Christmases with me whilst growing up on the farm.

Contents

Welcome to Christmas
on the Farm

When Dad pulled on his wellies, his old tweed jacket and his flat cap to do his morning rounds on the farm on Christmas Day, me and my sisters Libby, Becca and Lolo would all be begging to go with him. If the weather was not too bleak, he'd be happy to take us, and I like to think we were more of a help than a hindrance as we got older. For me, the youngest in the family, it started by being lifted on to the tailboard of the Land Rover as soon as I could toddle. We'd take it in turns chucking the hay out for the sheep and cows, and jumping down to open and close the gates. We'd have great fun with small lengths of bailer twine we found, tying them together into long strings and then dangling them off the back of the Land Rover, dragging them through the muddy tracks. The knots and the lumpy consistency of the mud made the strings wriggle about, and we called them snakes. It sounds like a cliché to say that children often prefer the box to the shiny present inside, but it illustrates how easy it is to make your own fun, and that is especially the case on a farm.

There is always something magical about Christmas on a farm, in a beautiful old farmhouse like ours at Bemborough, where my family has lived since my dad, Joe Henson, took over the tenancy in 1962. His parents weren't farmers, but he got the bug in his childhood and passed it down to me. The stone building lends itself to all the traditions of Christmas, and bedecked with holly and large bunches of mistletoe, with the wonderful smells of the traditional feast filtering from the kitchen, I feel especially connected to the generations of farmers who have gone before me, marking Christmas in much the same way through the centuries. The presents under the tree may have varied, but the need to look after the farm, and to celebrate the break, are unchanging.

I may be a familiar face from my various television programmes, most notably *Countryfile*, but first and foremost I am a farmer, involved in the day-to-day running of this farm in the beautiful, green Cotswold countryside, where the rolling hills are punctuated by villages of mellow stone. It is deservedly recognised as an Area of Outstanding Natural Beauty, and I am lucky enough to have lived here all my life.

The Cotswolds can look beautiful in the snow and the animals look striking when they're out in it – as you might think too, from looking at the cover of this book where I'm standing next to Ruby the Highland

Cow. But I may not be popular, especially with children, when I say the last thing I want, or any farmer wants, is a white Christmas. In December 2022 we had a big freeze, the coldest for more than ten years, and we all had to run around breaking the ice on the troughs and using a blowtorch to unfreeze pipes. Everywhere looked very pretty, but the animals don't like it and nor do we. If it happens over Christmas, when most of the staff are off and enjoying a deservedly good break at home, then it falls to me, my business partner Duncan and the senior management team – and anyone who lives close enough – to pitch in and give us a hand.

That's not to say I'd prefer it to be hot over Christmas. I have spent nearly all my Christmases at Bemborough, but there was one memorable Christmas when I was seven when we all flew out to Barbados. This sounds so upmarket, as though we lived in the realms of the wealthy who took to the skies to follow the sun in winter, but my childhood definitely wasn't like that! As a young man, when Dad first decided he wanted a career in farming, he went to Cirencester Agricultural College, and in those days students were housed together alphabetically, so Henson was billeted with Henderson and Hutson. They became good friends, as students do, and later on, when Dad was established at Bemborough, we were visited by his old college mates.

The Hutson family were involved in sugar cane production in Barbados, and they invited us over, which meant free accommodation if Mum and Dad could raise the money for the air fares. It was too big a chance to miss and John Neave, Dad's business partner, said that he could cope without Dad on the farm for one festive season, as Christmas is a relatively quiet period for farmers. Mum and Dad made lots of economies and we all accepted that our big present that year was the trip. Once we got to Barbados, we stayed in an outbuilding that had been converted into accommodation, and I remember it as a blissful time – although with one big drawback.

The Hutson family were members of the local yacht club, and one day we were invited there to go water skiing, which none of us had done before and was fantastic – I loved it. Mum was always careful to keep her ginger-haired son plastered in sun cream, but with the spray and the breeze I didn't feel as if I was burning, and it wasn't until the day was over that my whole back turned into one sheet blister. We had to get creams and potions from a local doctor. It was agony, and unfortunately for me people in Barbados are so friendly that there was a lot of back slapping and hugging going on . . . I still have a small scar on my back.

My dad was lucky to have his old school friend John Neave ('Uncle John') for a business partner, and I am just as lucky to have my business partner, Duncan Andrews, and a team of colleagues working with us. It means that, unlike the ancestors who worked the land before us, and for many farmers up and down the country today, none of us has to work the whole of Christmas

Day. Instead, I can settle down to Christmas dinner, my favourite meal, knowing I can fall asleep after if I wish!

There is nothing on that steaming plate that I don't love: turkey, sprouts, carrots, parsnips, roast potatoes, stuffing, gravy. It's particularly wonderful for me, and many other farmers, because we can look at the food in front of us and know where it has come from. I have experience of growing and raising some of the contents of the dinner plate, and have met many farmers who take care of the other ingredients – so I know from first-hand experience what has gone into it.

In this way, I have always felt a special connection with the season, but that's not the main reason I wanted to write this book. I wouldn't call myself a particularly sentimental man; farming is a tough business and you need to be pragmatic about it. But nor am I cold-hearted – the side of farming that has always interested me concerns animals, including the survival of rare breeds. Many of the stories you'll read in this book are about them.

And yet I think with age I've become softer and perhaps more sentimental. Since the arrival of my children, the death of my parents – and something that rocked our family to its core in recent years, which I'll share with you later in the book – Christmas has become ever more loaded with meaning. At the beginning of 2020, when the Covid-19 crisis forced us to close the Farm Park, I couldn't have dreamed we'd be able to open again by Christmas. When people of all ages streamed through the gates to follow our lights trail, the wonder of the festive period hit home. It's about being together. As a farmer, Christmas is a rare chance to slow down and think about how far we've come in the year and where to go next – but it's also about old traditions. When we celebrate in ways our parents did, we're keeping them alive. Those are the stories I want to share – stories that encapsulate what Christmas on a farm has been like for me and why it continues to be such a joyful time, long after the magic of childhood.

I don't want to give the impression that Christmas on farms is perfect though. Far from it – I'd like to make clear the difficulties the season brings so everyone understands what farmers up and down the country have to contend with. As I mentioned, winter can be tough for the animals – and for the other wild animals and wildlife that are so important to the natural world as a whole. Bad weather that goes on for too long can affect how crops grow in the spring; it really is a season where we're at the mercy of Mother Nature – she can create more drama than a soap opera.

For the Henson family, Christmas often seems to have been a time of personal near-misses, too. One year, when I was two, Dad came into the farmhouse one evening and said to Mum: 'Why is that boy out there on his own?'

'He isn't,' said Mum, perplexed. 'He's upstairs in his cot.'

Dad said he was sure he'd just heard me outside. They

both hurried out to check. One of my sisters (they're all older than me) had some school friends playing on the frosty lawn at the back of the house and were making a lot of noise so Mum thought that's what he must have heard. But Dad had been in the yard near the front of the house and was convinced he'd heard my voice from there. They couldn't spot me – until they looked up and gasped in horror. My bedroom was on this side of the house and there I was, suspended from the window by the elastic in my pyjama bottoms, which had caught on the window latch. Beneath me was a patio with some staddle stones. If I had fallen, I would have been badly injured. They reacted quickly, with Dad standing underneath to catch me in case I fell, and Mum rushing inside and up to my room to haul me back in.

Baffled as to how I got out, they put me back in my cot, and watched until I made my escape again. Apparently, I was climbing onto a chest of drawers and then up on to the windowsill. There had to be a hasty rearrangement of the furniture and a more secure fastening on the window. I have no memory of my Houdini escapade, but I've been told about it many times.

Another major Christmas near-disaster happened one Christmas Eve, when I was five. All the family was tucked up warm in bed while outside it was blowing a gale. Suddenly there was a loud bang and the whole house shook. Everyone woke and ran out of their bedrooms, bumping into each other on the landing. Dad peered out of one of the back windows that was itself shuddering in the wind, and announced that a tree was down and had hit the house. Mum, calm as ever, simply said that as we were all awake we should go downstairs for a cup of tea.

Dad took a torch, returning red-cheeked and wind-swept to report that the tree, a large beech, had come down onto my sister Lolo's bedroom, a branch driving through the roof of the dormer window, and damaging the main farmhouse roof and one of the chimneys.

The following day, Christmas Day, the weather had calmed down and the local builder/undertaker John Wright, a good family friend (he was known as Mighty Wrighty because he was a man of great stature) turned up with one of his workmen to cover the hole in the roof with a tarpaulin and check the rest of the roof was safe. It was very kind of him to come out at Christmas to help us, but that's often what small communities like ours can be like. Mighty Wrighty then reappeared once Christmas was over to fix it all properly.

Our landlord at the time was Corpus Christi College, Oxford, and they took their responsibilities seriously, sending out an expert to assess the other trees that were close to the farmhouse. One other beech had to be felled, and I remember standing with Mum watching the work in progress. The tree fell into the garden, but as we watched from the glassed-in porch, one of the upper limbs crashed down within a foot of where we were standing. It was a near miss!

I suppose what both those stories have in common

is my parents' ability to be calm in the face of a crisis, which is something I like to think they passed to me; as you'll see later, I've had to contend with a few crises of my own.

Despite any mishaps, Christmas on the farm was a special time in a special childhood. I feel very privileged to have grown up here, where I still live, and where I still celebrate Christmases with my own family. I imagine you're reading this at some point in the run-up to the festive period, or perhaps even on Christmas Day. Perhaps you are sitting by a fire, or with a blanket over your knees, a mug of something hot in hand. However you like to celebrate the holiday, I hope you enjoy these personal stories of mine, and I wish you and yours a very happy and healthy Christmas.

1

Christmas on the Henson Farm

When I was in the school nativity play, aged about five or six, I was appropriately chosen to play a shepherd. Mum was a talented dressmaker and she kitted me out beautifully, and I even had a miniature shepherd's crook. The crook was my undoing. As I came on stage I managed to get the tip of it stuck in a grating; the audience watched with bated breath and the whole production stalled as I tugged and tugged. So much for the show must go on, we were going nowhere until I rescued my crook . . . There was a tiny ripple of applause when it sprang free and the rest of the cast could proceed to the stable.

The feeling of embarrassment stayed with me for days, until Dad cheered me up by taking us to get the Christmas tree. When I was a child, this was always a big adventure. We lived close to a wood with mixed species of trees, including pines and firs. It wasn't on our land but was owned by our landlords, and with their permission Dad would make an annual expedition into the plantation.

Wrapped up warm in knitted jumpers and scarves, my sisters and I ran along at Dad's heels over the wet soil and leaves that hadn't yet mulched down. My three sisters and I arrived at two-year intervals, more or less. Libby (real name Elizabeth) is six years older than me, then comes Lolo (Louise) and, nearest in age to me, Rebecca (Becca). We fought from time to time but as the youngest, and the only boy, I was spoiled rotten. On the whole we got on incredibly well as children, and as adults we are still very close. They still tease me, but that's what big sisters do.

Dad was tall, athletic and lean. He never smoked, only drank very moderately, and usually had a stick in his hand, useful for moving livestock around and, when he got older, as a support. He always had a penknife in his pocket, vital for cutting bailer twine, and a flat cap on his head: he never left the house without his cap. That day, of course, he had a handsaw with him.

My sisters pointed at various trees along the woodland route, 'This one Dad?'

'Little too lopsided.'

'This one?'

'No, look there – it has too big a bald patch.'

Until eventually he looked down and me, with a twinkle in his eye. 'Adam, why don't you choose?'

He was very good at cheering me up. I chose the tree

and Dad sawed it down while Libby, Becca, Lolo and I looked on ready to shout 'Timber!', then we helped drag it back to the farmhouse. It was always, always too tall, and every year Mum would ask why we couldn't just choose one to fit, instead of having to chop a lump off the top of it. I never knew whether Dad did it deliberately . . .

Christmas trees have been around a long time, and nobody knows for sure where the idea of a tree in the house for Christmas originated, with Latvia and Estonia both claiming to be the first place public trees were erected and decorated. Bringing them into homes probably started with the German Protestants in the sixteenth century and then spread across Europe. When Prince Albert, who was German, married the young Queen Victoria it definitely gave the whole idea a boost here, especially among wealthy families. A bit of anti-German feeling after the First World War saw the popularity of the trees decline, but they quickly took off again and by the 1920s they were a large part of Christmas in all households, wealthy or poor, across the land. Now in the UK between eight and ten million real trees are sold each year. There's a big market in artificial trees, but I love the smell of a real tree. When you are buying one, it's a good idea to find one grown nearby, so that there is less transport damage to the environment, and most local councils will help by shredding the trees for wood chippings or compost after the Christmas celebrations are over.

When we got ours home we dragged it through to

the warm living room, dropping pine needles along the way for poor Mum to sweep up. Anchoring it in a large pot, we were able to get on with the exciting part. Out came the usual box of family decorations – lots of tinsel and an assortment of homemade baubles my sisters had made at school over the years, which I was now starting to add to. Most exciting were the chocolate decorations, which I would try to sneak off when nobody was looking, though Mum would always put them up high – out of the reach of any of our family dogs, who were always keen to sniff them out.

Being born on a farm I have grown up with dogs. We've had a succession, and the first was Chemmers, who Mum had before she married Dad; Chemmers was a nursemaid to me and my three sisters, treating us as if we were her own brood. She loved Mum, and as Mum clearly loved us, that was good enough for her. I don't remember her, because I was only two when she died, but I've heard how she watched over me as a baby. She was so accepting of us that when she had her own puppies she allowed my sister Libby to curl up in the basket with them, not something many feeding bitches would do.

Next to go up was the mistletoe. How tall Dad looked to me when I was that young, easily pinning bunches above almost every doorway, so that Mum was often having to lean up and give him a peck on the cheek, joking about how she couldn't wait for January when it would all come down.

'Ah but it's not just mistletoe,' would often be his response. 'Did you know that when gorse is in flower, that's the month for kissing?' Then he'd give a wink, because it's always possible to find gorse in flower somewhere throughout the year, even if it's only one lonely little yellow bloom. Mum would roll her eyes with a smile and swat him on the arm.

Mum was a strong character in her own right, but always supportive of Dad. She helped run the business, doing the books, paying the wages and handling the retail side of the Farm Park, as well as running the house. She was famously hospitable, and she loved to have a good laugh and throw a party. Her parties were renowned locally, and the farmhouse was always full at New Year or for birthdays. Unexpected guests did not faze her because she could rustle up a meal at any time. Unlike Dad, she was a smoker and she loved a drink. She always took pride in her appearance, her hair and makeup were always immaculate, ready for anyone who called in. It's from her that I inherited my red hair.

I love all the old lore around Christmas decorations, and mistletoe has played a part in many cultures over the centuries. Vikings believed mistletoe could raise people from the dead; when the god of the summer sun, Baldur the Beautiful, was killed by a poisoned sprig of mistletoe, his mother – the goddess of love and beauty – cried for her dead son and her tears changed the colour of the berries from red to white, and Baldur came back to life. After that, his mother kissed everyone who walked under the mistletoe out of gratitude for getting her son back.

In Greek mythology, Aeneas carried mistletoe to protect him when he visited the underworld, to make sure he could return. Druids believed it was a sacred plant, offering protection from evil and having magic powers. If they ever discovered it growing on an oak tree, which is very rare, they sacrificed two white bulls and feasted on them, sitting under the tree.

The Roman festival of Saturnalia, held between 17 and 23 December, involved couples kissing under mistletoe to bestow fertility on their marriage, and that belief has extended into more modern celebrations. An old English tradition says that a young woman who was not kissed under the mistletoe was destined not to marry for another year, but if she put a sprig under her pillow she would dream of the love of her life.

For centuries, farmers in parts of England and Wales saved the Christmas bunch of mistletoe that decorated their homes over the festival, to present it to the first cow that calved in the New Year, pinning it above her stall. The gift was considered an acknowledgement of her achievement and a guarantee that the whole herd would be fertile again for the next year. According to another legend, you can be sure of healthy cows and calves by hanging a sprig of holly in the cowsheds on Christmas Eve. Must remember to do both after Christmas this year!

Our ancestors probably associated fertility and

fruitful marriages with mistletoe because it doesn't have roots and therefore appears to reproduce spontaneously, which – before science came along to explain it – was interpreted as magical. It's also one of the few plants to bear fruit during winter, ahead of most others.

The truth is, mistletoe is actually a parasite (it's hemi-parasitic, to be precise, because although it gets its food from the host tree, it also uses photosynthesis to survive). Its seeds are distributed by birds, and people associate the Mistle Thrush with this, because of its name. It is true that thrushes are among a small number of birds that eat the white berries – most birds go for red or blue berries – but thrushes are not the most efficient seed dispersers. They eat the berry whole, seeds and all – which means the seeds are distributed when they come out of their other ends whole, too! Blackcaps, on the other hand (lovely little birds with distinctive songs) and Waxwings (which are larger), only eat the skin and pulp, wiping the seeds off with their beaks, onto the bark of the tree, which is more effective as the seed is deposited in the right location.

Because mistletoe is parasitic, it's even more important to harvest it (safely and legally) for a decoration at Christmas time. I've helped out with the mistletoe harvest quite a few times, including at an ancient apple orchard, not far from where we live in Gloucestershire. The trees were laden with the green leaves and the distinctive white berries, so much of it growing in such exuberant profusion that it was hard to make out the shape of the tree underneath. Under the guidance of Tim Andrews, who has spent the last ten years restoring orchards in Gloucestershire and making cider with the fruit of the apple trees he looks after, my job was to don some goggles, go up a ladder, and saw diagonally to release big branches – which I did after a bit of a struggle. The sad fact is that we have lost about 75 per cent of ancient apple orchards in my part of the country in the last fifty or sixty years, and although climate change and lack of pruning to keep the trees healthy are also culprits, mistletoe can kill trees if it is not kept in check. It particularly loves apple trees, and prefers them spaced out, as they are in traditional orchards, not in large commercial orchards. It has coexisted with the trees for centuries, but it needs to be controlled.

Tim told me that maintaining the orchards is more than just saving the trees; these old orchards are hosts to a great deal of biodiversity, with insects that are not found in commercial orchards. He explained that we were taking out branches of the tree so that it was less stressed, and the mistletoe was not given the chance to suck the life out of it.

When it came time to choose which mistletoe to take home with us, we were looking for the branches with the greenest leaves and the most berries. According to Jonathan Briggs, an expert on mistletoe who runs the website Mistletoe Matters, tradition says that you have to remove a berry for every kiss you have under the mistletoe, and when they're gone, so too are the kisses.

Christmas Eve in my childhood was all about getting excited for the day ahead. By then the house was fully decorated – although as late as the 1950s it was a country tradition that farmers would not decorate their homes until Christmas Eve itself, probably because that was the first time those hard-working families took any time off.

There would usually be family around the kitchen table if they were spending the following day with us. Bemborough Farm was a very popular Christmas destination for many friends and family, and Mum was always happy to have extra places around the table, guests filling all the spare beds. Uncle John, six-feet-two and also never without a cap, would often be there too, to wish us a Merry Christmas.

The smell of mince pies would permeate the house, and we'd be begging mum to try them while they were still hot. I know that traditionally Christmas Eve was a day of fasting in the Christian calendar, and a couple of hundred years ago nobody was allowed to eat until Sirius, which we call the dog star and is always the brightest in the winter sky, could be seen clearly. Thankfully we never had to wait that long; Mum always relented and handed them round.

Mince pies date back to the twelfth century, when

the Crusaders returned to this country with recipes for chopped meat (that's how we get the name mincemeat) pies flavoured with spices, particularly cinnamon, nutmeg and cloves, which were supposed to represent the gifts brought by the Wise Men. They were large pies, rectangular to represent the manger, and often with a pastry representation of the baby Jesus on top.

By the eighteenth century the meat filling was mainly tongue or tripe, but dried fruit and sugar were added and they were still often served alongside the savoury Christmas dinner, not separately as we do now. There's a superstition that says you should make a wish with the first mince pie you eat over the festive season, and that for real good luck in the year ahead you should eat one a day until Twelfth Night. Not too much of a hardship if you like mince pies, as I do.

When we were small, we woke up very excited, as all children do, on Christmas morning. At the ends of our beds were white fishermen's socks, bulging and distorted by the collection of little treats inside them. We always piled onto Mum and Dad's bed to open them, and I remember getting down to the tangerine and walnut at the bottom with a slight feeling of disappointment, because the surprises were over.

After the opening of the stockings, it was time to pull on the wellies and waterproofs to do the rounds of the animals: sheep, cattle, pigs, horses and the hens in the farmyard. A couple of hours running around outside is a great start to Christmas morning, and then it was back to the kitchen, collecting the new-laid eggs on the way, trying to remember to take our boots off before we trailed mud over the kitchen floor, in time for a late breakfast. Soon afterwards the adults would crack open the sherry – Mum loved a sherry at any time, but especially at Christmas – while we got down to the serious and exciting business of opening our presents.

Money was clearly tight in the early days, and many farmers today struggle to make ends meet. They have to contend with the rising cost of fuel, machinery and labour, as well as the volatility of competing in a world market, constantly having to compare prices from around the world. But back then Mum never made us aware of how hard it was for them, making a great many of our Christmas presents herself because she was an excellent seamstress. She specialised in wonderful stuffed toys, including a guardsman soldier with a large busby head-dress for one of my sisters.

My favourite was a four-feet-long stuffed crocodile, made of green velvet. I can remember being puzzled by what could be inside this large, strange-shaped present, and thrilled when I found him. I called him – unimaginatively – Crocodile, and for a time I insisted on taking this long, green toy everywhere with me. If ever our very hospitable farmhouse had thirteen people round the table, Crocodile was given a place, too, to ward off bad luck.

I loved the feel of the velvet; as a very small child I could not get to sleep without sniffing something soft or furry. I used to suck two fingers – never my thumb – and have some soft fabric against my nose; Mum made me toys with patches of rabbit fur or something similar to soothe me. When I didn't have a comforter, Dad would go out into the yard, round up one of the chickens who roosted in the beams, and ignoring its indignant protests, pull out a feather! As parents all know, you do anything to get a little one to sleep.

My mum inherited her seamstress skills from her mum, who was a very good dressmaker. Nana and Grampy were Welsh, and when I was growing up they lived in Cheltenham, where they had a sweet shop. Imagine: a small boy whose grandparents had a sweet shop ... it was wonderful, and I'm afraid I've grown up with a real sweet tooth – and a mouthful of fillings to prove it.

I remember Nana's table was always covered with paper patterns and bolts of fabric. She'd taught my mum so well that on top of making our clothes, Mum also made our Uncle Nicky's, who was a regular at our house on Christmas Day.

Uncle Nicky was better known as the acclaimed actor Nicky Henson, my dad's younger brother, and even as children we knew there was something glamorous and different about him. But for us, he was just great fun to be around. As you might know, I'm part of a showbusiness dynasty. Dad tried to turn his back on the family legacy, a career that involved performing – only to end up introducing his beloved animals on television quite regularly. If he had followed his father, as I followed him, he would never have become a farmer, but would have taken to the stage like Nicky did, because Dad's father, Leslie Henson, was a very well-known actor, comedian and impresario.

Dad became interested in farming instead because when he and his mum lived in Northwood, last stop on the Metropolitan line of the London Underground, it was still a rural area, with a small farm just along the road where Shire horses were still used for ploughing, and milking was done by hand. Dad loved going there, and as soon as he was old enough he spent his free time working there, collecting eggs for the farmer. It was the basis of his ambition to farm, and especially gave him his love for the old farming traditions.

Nicky, on the other hand, followed the family tradition, and after leaving school went to RADA to train as a stage manager, switching to becoming an actor. He was very successful for five decades, on stage with the National Theatre, the Royal Shakespeare Company, in films, in musicals and on television.

Nicky was very good looking, and his best friend, actor Ian Ogilvy, was also dashingly handsome. These two young actors cut a swathe through the swooning actresses of the West End, and I still today occasionally meet actresses of a certain vintage who go misty-eyed when I mention that Nicky was my uncle. Joanna

Lumley once said to me, 'Oooh, I certainly remember Nicky and The Og,' which was the nickname for Ian Ogilvy.

A couple of years after I was born, Nicky married Una Stubbs, an actor just as famous and successful as he was, appearing later as Aunt Sally in the *Worzel Gummidge* series and more recently as Mrs Hudson, the housekeeper to Benedict Cumberbatch's Sherlock Holmes. Uncle Nicky and Una had two sons together, my cousins Christian and Joe, both of whom are successful musicians and composers today.

Nicky was a frequent visitor to Bemborough Farm, and when I was about eleven he lived with us for a time while appearing with the Royal Shakespeare Company in Stratford-on-Avon. I think it was a great escape for him from his glamorous but slightly mad life in London. Sometimes he'd just bomb down on his own, on his motorbike, but at other times he would come with his family.

In my early Christmases, they would often be with us – along with Billie, Nicky and Dad's mum, my grandmother. Billie was a regular visitor to Bemborough farm when I was young. The Christmas I got my shepherd's crook caught on stage was her last – she'd moved in with us as her health declined, and my saintly mum nursed her in her last months. She had throat cancer, from a lifetime of smoking, and I remember seeing Mum help her up the stairs. I think Billie was a powerful lady, a force to be reckoned with, and it took a lot of patience and forbearance on Mum's part. I was too little to be aware of the friction; Billie was always lovely to me, hugging and kissing me whenever I went to her room to see her.

After presents came lunch, after lunch came the Queen's speech as it then was (Dad was a great Royalist, and having been a boy during the Second World War he was unashamedly patriotic), after the Queen's speech came games. Charades is played by families everywhere as one of the great Christmas traditions, and when I was growing up it was a favourite part of the Christmas break. Here at the farm we took this simple game to a whole different level: playing charades with my family, especially with Uncle Nicky and Auntie Una in the room, was like watching an acting masterclass. Although Dad followed his own star to become a farmer not an entertainer, he ended up collecting plenty of television credits to his name as a presenter so he, too, was used to being centre stage. Mum, who was a schoolteacher before she married Dad and had a much less exotic family background, was also no mean performer, and she and Dad, I swear, had a telepathic way of communicating with each other.

They were all brilliant at the game so we had to make it increasingly harder. Shakespeare plays were too easy – they would be signalled by holding an imaginary spear in the air and shaking it, after which it would take the thespians only a minute or two to identify the play from the number of words.

It became such a fast game, with answers called out before the mime could really get started, that we scrapped the 'book, play, film, television show' categories, and started miming random five-word phrases, the more bizarre the better.

'Pink men enjoy dancing flamenco.'

'Angry frog leapt under car.'

'Architect fell over skipping rope.'

You had to be very expressive acting it out, sticking strictly to the rules about showing the others the number of words, syllables and so on. Taking part meant you were completely in the spotlight, and with pro-actors looking on you definitely couldn't be shy and sit in a corner, which, although I didn't know it, may have provided me with some sort of training for my later television career. My sisters were all very good at it, and competitive, although we always ended collapsing in giggles together.

None of us knew this at the time but I've since looked it up: our way of playing – miming random phrases – was more in line with the original charades game which was invented in France in the eighteenth century. It has evolved over the years, but once again the Hensons were doing their bit to preserve the DNA of its ancestor, just as we have tried to do with our rare breeds animals.

We usually had a small dinner of leftovers in the evening – before or after which Dad would see to the animals again. Then the adults would put us to bed. I'm sure I would have heard them laughing downstairs – with Mum drinking more sherry and Dad, who never drank much, having a glass of beer – but the clearer memories I have are of the owls that nested in the mature beech woodland behind the farmhouse. As a child, their soothing hoots were often the last things I heard before I fell asleep.

2

Not Just for Christmas

M y eighth Christmas was particularly special.
The festive period started as it always did, on
the last Sunday of November: Stir-up Sunday. That's
the traditional day to make Christmas pudding and
it's when Mum made it every year. Wearing one of her
colourful aprons, she'd assemble all the ingredients on
the large, scrubbed table in the long farmhouse kitchen,
with a traditional old Aga and a tiled floor which Mum
was constantly mopping because of all the dogs and
muddy boots. There were always a couple of Cotswold
Farm Park tea towels drying on the Aga.

My sisters and I took it in turns to stir the pudding
and make a wish as we did so. I don't remember my
wishes on any of the other years (they were probably
to do with homework and my wish never to have to
do it), but I do on that one, because it was the year it
came true.

Once Mum had popped in the silver sixpence, she put
the muslin-wrapped pudding onto boil and the kitchen

steamed up as it bubbled away. For the weeks that followed, I thought about my wish, not telling anyone – as every child knows, if you tell your wish, it is guaranteed not to come true.

By this point in my life – 1974 – Bemborough farm had changed quite a bit. When Dad and Uncle John took over the tenancy they originally ran it as an arable farm. It was remarkable, because neither of them had a farming background, but they were determined to make a go of it. Farming was what Dad wanted to do, but fields of crops didn't really satisfy him; he wanted a farm stocked with animals. This was not generally considered the best way to operate a business on the Cotswolds land they farmed, but for him, a landscape needed to be populated with animals.

It would have been easier to simply add a small flock of commercial sheep and a few cows, which they did, but Dad had always had a fascination with the ancient breeds of animals that were first farmed in the British Isles, right back to the Iron Age settlers who first started breeding and looking after livestock in order to feed their families. Dad knew that many of the ancient breeds, those who in their genes carry the history of Britain, were facing extinction, and he wanted to do whatever he could to help them. Some people play golf as a hobby, some tinker with old cars, some become amateur photographers; from childhood, Dad wanted to look after animals, endangered native species in particular, and this was, at first, his hobby.

These animals were out of fashion because, on the whole, they were slow to grow and did not produce as much meat as more modern crossbreeds, which were often brought in from abroad and bred intensively, their whole lives managed by farmers and vets to be the best possible money-spinners. There is nothing wrong with this, it's vital for farms to be financially viable, but Dad was worried that if we let whole breeds die out we would lose more than the sentimental value of keeping them alive. They could, he believed, be a very useful research tool for scientists in the future. It was very far-sighted of him, because nobody knew much about genetics (DNA was only discovered in 1953). Besides all that, he just loved the look of them. To him, they were what a farm should look like.

He and John agreed to take on the rare breeds that were being temporarily housed at Whipsnade Zoo, in Hertfordshire, where they were being preserved as 'a living gene bank'. Native breeds are part of our national identity and heritage, and keeping them going has implications for disease resistance, food security, and preserving natural habitats. Making sure they did not die out, so that their genes were available for the future, was a concept Dad endorsed, and which is still one of our aims today. He and John set about converting pastures and stable buildings for the rare breeds of cattle and sheep which became the basis of our collection.

The original breeds that came to Bemborough, when I was five, were Highland, Longhorn, White Park, Belted Galloway and Dexter cattle, plus three breeds of sheep: Soay, Jacobs and Portland, and one Norfolk ram. Although I was very young, I remember the excitement as the lorries pulled in and the animals were unloaded. To add to this initial collection, Dad had already bought a couple of Gloucester cows and two Gloucestershire Old Spot pigs, a breed that was fast heading for extinction.

Soon after they arrived in 1971, Dad decided to open our collection of animals to the public, setting up 'The Cotswold Farm Park', which was the first Farm Park in the world and had two objectives: to preserve and rescue ancient breeds of farm animals, and to educate and inspire people. Dad wanted to share his knowledge and enthusiasm with as many people as possible, because he knew this was the best way to conserve the breeds. If people cared about them, they would support protecting them. The descendants of those first animals are still at the Farm Park today. Although I was too young to understand the science, even then I was imbued with a feeling that he was doing something important that I wanted to be part of.

Then in 1973, Dad was one of the founders – and became the first chairman – of the Rare Breeds Survival Trust. It brought together all the rare breed enthusiasts from across the country to work in a more organised way to identify animals that were heading for extinction without help. From 1900 to 1973, twenty-six native

British breeds became extinct, but from the day the Trust was founded, no more have been lost, and Dad shares the credit for this.

I have great memories of walking around the rare breeds at the Farm Park, Dad telling me where they came from and what their unique traits were. To me, at that age, it was just what farming was about, and I understood why he loved these special animals. When Dad started doing lambing in front of the public at the Farm Park, Libby and I would help out, with Dad providing a running commentary. I also helped with the milking demonstrations, thankfully with a placid Gloucester cow, who was happy to be milked in front of an appreciative audience.

It was because of the Farm Park that Dad became a well-known face on TV. When the Farm Park first opened, Dad was 'discovered' by television when a programme came to film the rare breeds, and the producer recognised Dad was a natural in front of a camera – his enthusiasm when he talked about the animals spilled over to the viewers.

After that, Dad became a regular on a TV programme called *Animal Magic*, presented by Johnny Morris – if Johnny wanted an animal that wasn't an exotic foreign zoo exhibit but a familiar one that children could see in fields around the country, Dad was called into the studios in Bristol. Lots of our animals had their moment of stardom in front of the camera, although they were unfazed by their fame!

When Dad took on a much bigger commitment for the BBC, travelling the world to film farmed animals that had gone feral, we had to get used to him being away filming – and to him being a minor celebrity. As we walked around the Farm Park with him he would be stopped by visitors, wanting to chat to him. Now it happens to me, but today it's always a snap on a phone.

Our farm attracted attention from other media quarters too – I remember when an advertising agency turned up to make one of the famous Milky Bar Kid ads, which ran from the 1960s to the 1990s. The Milky Bar Kid – a blond bespectacled boy dressed in a cowboy suit – had to ride into the farmyard on a cart being pulled by one of our Shire horses.

As he passed a stable, a cow had to put her head over the half-door and moo, then he shouted the famous line: 'The Milky Bars are on me!' Sounds simple enough, but the only way Dad could get the cow to moo was to put her calf at the other side of the yard. Then she was held back until the cart was passing. It took quite a few takes to get what the producer wanted, and Dad was being very careful to make sure the cow and her calf did not get stressed. I was quite young at the time, but the best bonus was a box full of Milky Bars that Mum rationed out on special occasions.

I was allowed one of the Milky Bars instead of the usual mince pies that Christmas Eve, and remembered my wish back on Stir-up Sunday, wondering if it was going to come true.

The next day, after we'd opened our stockings, seen to the animals and had our breakfast, we were sitting in the living room for our presents. One at a time, my sisters ripped the wrapping paper off their toys until there were no more gaudy packages under the Christmas tree. I began to feel forgotten. Uncle Nicky and Una were there and had been their usual generous selves; they had the classic fluctuating finances of professional actors, but when they were in funds we all got lovely presents from Harrods. We were brought up not to be materialistic, but it was great at times to feel the glamour of London was coming to Bemborough. Nicky was always happy to spend money – he loved motorbikes, he dressed very trendily, and he liked a good night out; such a contrast with Dad and his ancient tweed jackets smelling of damp and sheep, and whose idea of a good night was round the fire with his family.

But there had been no present from Mum and Dad for me. I was too old to think that Father Christmas had by-passed me for not being a good boy all year, but I was worried. Why was I the only one without a present, when one of my sisters had a bike and the other two had musical instruments that they were now noisily practising at playing?

Mum, seeing my serious face, said: 'Look over there, Adam.'

In the corner of the living room was an old, battered tea chest with a piece of Christmas paper stuck across the top instead of a lid.

'Open it,' she said, smiling, and she and Dad came to stand by me as I tore off the red paper. There, looking up at me, was a small liver and white springer spaniel. She stared at me with her big brown eyes and I gazed down at her, and in that moment an incredible bond was formed, one that would last all her long life. Tears sprang to my eyes, I was so moved by the sight of her. She was exactly what I had wished for.

I wasn't tall enough to reach down to her, so Dad gently lifted her and placed her in my arms. She immediately snuggled into my chest, turning her head up and gently licking my face. She was the most beautiful puppy I had ever seen, and she grew to be the most wonderful, devoted dog any boy could ever own.

She was eight weeks old and small for her breed: she must have been the smallest in the litter. Mum and Dad had picked her up from the breeder the night before and somehow kept her a secret. She had made no noise as I watched my sisters opening their presents, given no clue to being nestled down on a blanket in an old chest. It must have been so strange for her, away from her mother and brothers and sisters and surrounded by the new smells and noises of the farmhouse, but she was a brave little soul, then and always. With help from the rest of the family, I decided to call her Nita. Dad was very fond of his Aunt Nita, who lived near us and was a familiar face on the farm, and the name seemed to suit my little friend.

By this time, Mum's Lab, Chemmers, who she'd had

long before we children were born, had died. We'd taken in a couple of dogs from Dad's friend who was emigrating to Australia – another black Labrador, Trudy, and an elderly springer spaniel called Ben. Though Ben had sadly died, too, he was the first springer I knew, and my parents could see that I really liked the look of him, and that was why my Christmas present was the little springer.

After presents came the Feast – and what a feast. We had all the traditional food: turkey, roast potatoes, sprouts, carrots, stuffing and loads of gravy, extra helpings for anyone with a big appetite, followed by Mum's lucky Christmas pudding.

But for once, I wasn't interested in pulling crackers and competing with my sisters for the silver sixpence in the pudding, I wanted the Christmas dinner to be over as soon as possible. Mum and Dad had strict rules for dogs, and I was not allowed to cradle her on my lap as I ate. Besides, as Mum gently pointed out to me, she was only a baby, and babies need to sleep, as well as to play. Still, it was very hard not to keep making excuses to go back into the kitchen to stroke her silky ears.

Why do we have such a blowout feast at Christmas? Apart from the religious significance of the date, why is it also associated with the biggest banquet in our calendar?

A midwinter feast goes back thousands of years,

right to Neolithic times. We know from the work of archaeologists exploring sites near Stonehenge that pigs and cattle were killed for feasting, and from the age of the pig's teeth that have been found, it's clear they were about nine months old, so if they were born in spring they were slaughtered for a feast, probably at the mid-winter solstice, which occurs on 21 or 22 December, pretty close to our Christmas. While the pigs were spit roasted, the beef was made into stews, and there's evidence our Stone Age ancestors also ate crab apples, hazelnuts, sloes and blackberries.

The celebration was almost certainly associated with the shortest day of the year, when the sun was least visible, and the bonfires and feasting heralded the start of the days getting longer. Our word 'yule' comes from the Old Norse 'houl', meaning wheel, because the Norsemen believed the sun was a wheel that kept turning, and they ate and drank to celebrate it starting the return journey to better weather and longer days.

The Romans had a wild midwinter festival, Saturnalia, lasting seven days, and people famously drank too much and behaved badly, and gave each other presents. Not too different to our celebrations today.

Moving on to England in the fourteenth century, we know from monastery records that although the monks and nuns ate sparsely during the year, and their food was bland and uninspiring, in the week leading up to Christmas there was a change of gear. Spices were used to improve the taste, and apart from the usual diet of fish and poultry, there was roast beef, pork, venison and meat pies, with a healthy monk consuming up to 7,000 calories each day during the celebrations. That's about three times what they needed, but we can't criticise because estimates put our Christmas day intake at between 5–7,000. It's a good job it's only once a year. And while the rest of the year they drank beer or mead, at Christmas the prosperous monasteries were spending a small fortune importing good wine from France.

The nobility in their castles were also eating very well, with large feasts including stuffed boars' heads and roast peacock. Bread was served at all meals, often used as a plate, or trencher, for the more exciting food to be served on. This soggy bread would then be given to the poor when the meal was over.

In Tudor times the traditional beef and venison was supplemented by badger, blackbirds and woodcock. This was when turkey was introduced from North America. The first record of turkeys here is in 1526, when a man called William Strickland brought some back from his travels and sold them in Bristol. Some of their smaller ancestors were introduced years earlier by the Spanish, but it was the turkeys from North America that soon became regarded as great delicacies. Most of them were imported by Turkish traders, which explains why they got the name 'turkey'. They were bigger and plumper than chickens, and they tasted better than swans or peacocks.

Wealthy Tudors also pioneered a speciality Christmas

pie, which was a pigeon, inside a partridge, inside a chicken, inside a goose, inside a turkey, served in a pastry case. It's an idea that had become fashionable again in recent years, although we usually stick to a three-bird roast, with no pastry. I've never been tempted by the idea; nothing beats turkey, especially the dark meat on the leg. I'm slightly baffled by people who prefer a turkey crown; for me, they are missing the best bits.

What do you like to drink with your meal? I definitely envy our ancestors the tradition of making a large bowl of punch to offer a toast to the crops in the fields and the fruit trees for the coming year. As a farmer with fields of crops and an orchard I would certainly drink to that! The punch that was passed around at the Christmas feast in days of yore was usually ale mixed with the same sort of spices we use to make mulled wine, and it would have been served warm, too.

Personally, we like to have sparkling wine. It was making a *Countryfile* programme that converted me to English sparkling wines. Like most people, I had no idea how well they have developed over the years, but now they are my first choice for any sparkling celebration fizz, and to prove how good they are I took some bottles right behind the enemy lines, to France. The idea that England can produce wine to challenge the French was too good an opportunity to miss, so I dressed up as a wine waiter (I could use the French word sommelier, but that implies more knowledge of wine than I can claim). In a blind tasting on the street, I persuaded tourists to sample the English sparkling wine made by Nyetimber, the biggest English producer. Everyone loved the English wine, most of them preferring it to champagne (we can't call the English wine champagne, because for that it has to come from the Champagne region of France). I have to admit I was surprised to discover that I also preferred the English sparkling wine, and from then on Nyetimber has become our favourite celebration drink at home.

For the programme we were given permission to take our bottles into the famous champagne house, Pol Roger, whose champagne was Winston Churchill's favourite tipple. Pol Roger has been in business for 170 years and is still run by the same family. We met the chief sommelier – he can use that name because he really *does* know what he is talking about – who took us into their amazing tasting room, all marble and brass, the walls lined with champagne bottles. He refused to do blind tasting – think how terrible it would have been if the English wine had won! Still, he was happy to try the Nyetimber, and give us his opinion. He smiled haughtily as he gave a Gallic shrug and declared, 'It is very good for a first try . . .' In other words: not, in his opinion, a true competitor, and he was telling the Brits to get back in their box. But judging by the ordinary people who tried it on the street, and the reaction of my friends and family when I serve it, it is a lot more than a good try.

Nyetimber is one of a growing number of English vineyards and wine makers which are earning international respect. Interestingly, there was a vineyard on the same spot in West Sussex as the Nyetimber headquarters mentioned in the Domesday Book, when there were forty vineyards across Britain, mostly making the wine for church communion. Wine making in some form dates from much earlier, even before the Romans, who were partial to sweet, fruity wines, and set about growing their own grapes when they were occupying Britain. Without preservatives, wine from their homeland didn't travel well, so they made their own in Britain.

Ordinary people drank ale or mead in those days. There was a small but steady wine-making culture until the mid-nineteenth century, when it became cheaper and simpler to import wine from France, Spain and Portugal. What vineyards were left were ploughed up for crop production during the First World War, and it wasn't until the mid-twentieth century that vineyards started to spring up again. In 1988 Nyetimber opened, planting the varieties of grapes used for making champagne. They were part of a movement that pioneered English sparkling wines, which now make up the backbone, about 70 per cent, of our wine production.

The company now has vineyards in Sussex, Hampshire and Kent. With the climate warming up (fourteen of the warmest twenty summers on record have occurred since the millennium), the prospect for English viticulture looks good, and today grape vines are grown as far north as Yorkshire and Lancashire.

I have heard of a few farmers who are diversifying into vines to supply the growing wine industry. Sadly, our soil is too thin and, being high, our winter frosts too harsh to make it a viable proposition for us. The drawback for all those diversifying into it is that it takes three to four years for the first crop, and then months more to mature the wine, but as an extra string to their bow, I think it could be a winning idea, as long as demand for wine remains high.

I'm not a wine snob, and I'm not just a wine drinker. There's nothing better than a pint of good English beer, and we're very happy to collaborate with a brewery that has the same aspirations that we do at the farm: sustainable, local produce. We grow Maris Otter barley, the only brewing barley solely grown in the UK, and so much prized that brewers of craft beers sometimes put the words 'Maris Otter barley' on their labels, an accolade that tells real beer experts that the resulting brew is rather special. It really is the Rolls-Royce of malting barley. The seed is controlled, and only approved farms are allowed to grow it; thankfully we make the grade.

We made a *Countryfile* programme where I followed our spring malting barley by lorry to the port, across to Germany, and then up the Rhine to the maltsters, and then to the brewery. Afterwards Duncan and I talked it through and decided we ought to work with a brewery here in the UK, to cut back on the travel, to support a smaller, local brewery, and make more of our Maris Otter.

We looked around for some time to find a brewer we thought would appreciate our barley and the ethos in which it is grown – a crop that helps Bemborough towards a sustainable future. In 2012 we found the perfect match in Butcombe Brewery, a Bristol-based company dedicated to preserving all the great traditions of British brewing. They have been taking our barley ever since, and we were thrilled when they developed, with our input, Rare Breed Pale Ale, its name a tribute to our work with rare breed animals. As a bottled beer it won awards, and now it's in barrels, too, so you can buy it on draught in pubs, which is just right after a day's work outdoors. Recently they've developed Cotswold Ram Ale, which is stronger and darker, and I'd be pushed to say which I prefer.

On Christmas Day, though, it's definitely the sparkling wine that accompanies our blowout feast.

Back to the Christmas I was given Nita; as soon as I could get away from the table, I lay down next to her, watching the gentle rise and fall of her chest, listening to her snuffling breath.

Dogs in our house were very well loved but they knew their place, which was not on the furniture and definitely not upstairs. However, that night, after everyone was asleep, I lay awake listening to a faint whimpering from the kitchen and, unable to bear the thought that she was unhappy, I sneaked downstairs and brought her up to my bedroom, where she settled down pressed against me and we both slept well.

I intended to get up early and take her downstairs before anyone was around, but Mum beat me to it and came into the bedroom where we were curled up together. I pretended to be asleep, fearing a good telling off, but neither she nor Dad had the heart to enforce the rule, and from then on, whenever I was at home, my little dog slept with me, with Mum and Dad turning a blind eye, and the other dogs in the house accepting that it was a privilege just for her.

That Christmas Day was, and is, one of the best days ever in my memory.

3

Winter Care for Livestock

I was ten years old, hanging on for dear life to a huge tarpaulin laden with hay bales and animal feed, which was being dragged across the snowbound fields by a steady, plodding, good-natured shire horse called Kitty. Sun Ray, another beautiful shire, was pulling another improvised sledge. It was a freezing winter, with heavy snowfall across the country. The Cotswolds were enveloped in it, and our high farm had more than its share, the landscape altered beyond recognition by the billowing drifts. It made for a lovely picturesque Christmassy scene, great for children to play in, wonderful material for photographers to capture on film, but a nightmare for farmers with livestock to feed and keep watered.

My sisters and I were now big enough to help Dad out in the emergency, but his biggest help by far came not from his children but from Kitty and Sun Ray, who demonstrated to us all that old-fashioned, outmoded farming methods take some beating when the going gets tough. The horses were huge but gentle, and their massive feet made the most effective snowshoes. Unable to get a tractor to the fields, Dad had fashioned chains to the tarpaulins and attached them to the collars and harnesses of the Shires. Our makeshift sledges, laden with fodder for the sheep and cattle in the farm fields and with hay bales round the sides to stop everything – including us – falling off, lurched as the snow concealed hidden dips in the land. We kids squealed with delight when we were occasionally thrown into a drift and had to scramble back on board, but Kitty and Sun Ray never faltered.

The banks of snow were so big that when we reached the boundary to one field, where a stone wall separated it from the next, the horses were able to drag us uphill and across the wall without floundering. It was great fun for us youngsters, but a very serious business for Dad, and even more so for the stranded animals in need of food.

We expected deep snow every year, although now, because of climate change, it happens only occasionally. Mum always had the larder stocked for a month-long siege in the winter. That year we dug out a couple of sheep who had managed to wade into the drift and were out of their depth, but it was rare for us to lose any sheep, as we were always prepared as far as possible for the winter months. The sheep were moved into fields close to the farmyard; they stay out in the fields rather than in barns because in most weathers they are able to feed off the grass, with only supplementary feeding of hay. Cattle are heavy, and their feet churn up the ground around the feeders and make a real mess; sheep are much lighter, and don't congregate in the same way. Dad would supplement the grass with hay in racks that Uncle John had made (so sturdily that we still have some of them today), and his flock of Southdown sheep would make use of these metal structures to give their backs a good scratch. By rubbing along the rack they dislodged seeds from the hay, which fell into their fine, close fleeces along their broad backs. One year, to our great surprise, the following spring the sheep sprouted a crop of green grass, growing in their wool. Ever conscious of making the most of opportunities to publicise the Farm Park, Dad put a rabbit on their backs to eat the grass. It made a great picture for the local paper, under the headline 'Double Decker Farming'.

Whichever field we put the sheep in over winter was the one with the best access for a tractor in case the snow was bad – except, of course, when only a Shire horse could get through . . .

As I've said, Dad had first seen Shire horses working when, as a teenager, he helped out on the farm close to his home, where heavy horses were used to plough and pull wagons and where there were old breeds of pigs and cattle. It was there that Dad first came across the idea of preserving these rare and dying breeds, which eventually led to setting up the Farm Park. That Christmas, Kitty and Sun Ray more than proved his point to us all. They were going where no tractor or any mechanised vehicle could go.

Kitty was one of several Shire horses Dad owned, and she had an impressive pedigree; we called her Kitty but her real name was 'Culcliffe Modern Maid'. The breed has been in existence since the late 1700s, when a native heavy horse, the Lincolnshire Black, was crossed with horses from the Netherlands to create 'the great horse of the English Shires'. Sadly, the Lincolnshire Black died out about 150 years ago, or I'm sure Dad would have found some for our rare breeds collection.

Shires were the next best thing, and we had a few over the years, using them on the farm as well as for visitors to marvel at. The description 'gentle giants' is completely appropriate. The stallions can be up to six-feet tall to their shoulders, with the mares often over five feet in height up to their shoulders, or 'withers' to use the correct term. They tower over me. They have tremendous strength, with a record set in the 1920s by a pair of Shires who pulled a load of forty-five tons (although that figure is imprecise, because the scales could not cope with anything heavier). There is nothing more impressive than seeing a shire horse at work, its coat glistening chestnut and black, the harness gleaming, and its mane and tail sometimes plaited with ribbons.

A couple of years later, in 1978, Sun Ray would become one of the most famous horses in Britain when she modelled for the very talented wildlife and animal artist Patrick Oxenham, for a set of commemorative postage stamps celebrating 100 years of the Shire Horse Society. Three other horses also featured on the stamps: a Welsh pony, a Shetland pony and a thoroughbred racehorse, but on the special first edition pack, the main painting was Sun Ray, with her traditional leather and brass collar and harness, with an old-fashioned plough behind. I have a set of the first day covers of the stamps.

Sun Ray belonged to Joanna Neave, Uncle John's wife. Uncle John and Joanna loved their heavy horses, which they kept at the farm. Joanna was the Matron at Cheltenham General Hospital; a very organised, capable woman, and very loving towards us kids. I've since met people who worked with her, and they've all told me that she was the very best of traditional hospital Matrons: she ran everything very efficiently, but she was very caring towards all the patients and staff. We soon learned not to tell her if we had a wobbly tooth because she'd whip it out – wallop – before you knew what was happening!

We were all excited about Sun Ray being chosen to model for the stamps because we knew this kind and gracious animal would be completely unfazed by her moment in the spotlight. She went on to star in a TV documentary, *All the Queen's Horses*, where Patrick was filmed sketching her. Patrick is no longer with us, but his son and daughter-in-law are also artists, and run a gallery in Herefordshire showcasing his and their works.

The wonderful thing about Shire horses is that they love working. They are by temperament eager to please, they get on with each other because they are by nature peaceable, they like nothing better than being given a job to do. In the past they delivered heavy goods, famously pulling a brewers' dray full of barrels of beer, they towed canal barges, they pulled coaches and trams, and during the First World War they went to the Western front to tow gun carriages and heavy munitions and supplies. Back then there were an estimated one million Shire horses working in the UK, now there are fewer than 3,000 – but 'horsepower' is still the unit we use to measure the power of an engine and it is a fitting tribute to these amazing animals.

I love an old poem, that I first heard recently:

'The Horse' by Ronald Duncan
Where in this wide world can
man find nobility without pride,
Friendship without envy or beauty
without vanity? Here, where
grace is laced with muscle, and
strength by gentleness confined.
He serves without servility; he has
fought without enmity. There is
nothing so powerful, nothing less
violent, there is nothing so quick,
nothing more patient.
England's past has been borne on
his back. All our history is his
industry; we are his heirs, he
our inheritance.

*

Once we'd done all we could for the animals out in the snowy fields, we took Kitty and Sun Ray back to their stables. Over winter they were given extra hay because they had such large bodies to maintain. We also had two riding ponies belonging to my sisters at the time, which would stay in the stables when the weather was bad, with rugs on their backs to keep them warm.

Then Dad and I went to check in on the other animals – cattle and pigs – housed in the barn, which we did every day. Every couple of days we would have to lay down fresh straw on top of what was there, and a couple of times every winter we would bring the animals out for a morning and use a JCB to shovel out the muck and start again with fresh straw.

One of those animals was Miracle the Dexter calf. We'd called her Miracle, because that's what she was – a real miracle.

Dexters are a miniature breed of cattle, sturdy and black; bred for their meat, but so cute to look at that they are occasionally kept as pets. We didn't have a big herd, only half a dozen or so.

There's an area on our farm called The Cemetery, probably because it is an ancient burial place. It's a patch of rough grass and scrubland, surrounded by arable fields used to grow crops. To keep the rough vegetation down Dad periodically took the Dexters and all our rare breed cattle to The Cemetery to graze, because they were happy eating scrub and bushes.

One chilly day back in spring, I had gone with Dad to

53

bring the Dexters back from the cemetery. We rounded them up and walked them back to the farmyard. Dad was always teaching me about animals, and he pointed to one of the cows and said:

'That one's about to give birth. You can see her udders are swollen, she's getting ready to feed her calf.'

Dad put her in a loose box and waited a couple of days, and she had still not given birth. She was bellowing a bit and seemed restless, so Dad was worried that something was wrong, and he called the vet. The vet examined her and pronounced: 'This cow is empty. She has already calved.'

Dad was really upset, because it meant that we had brought the herd back and left her calf behind. We reckoned it might have been premature and died at birth or, if not, it would certainly have died by this time. Dad, my sister Libby and me set off at once to try to find the calf, feeling pretty miserable as we expected to find its body.

As we searched the scrubland a roe deer rose from close in front of us and bounded away, her white rear bobbing up and down. We were quite used to deer on our land, and the cemetery was an area they used for cover, but as we drew level with the bush it had sprung from we noticed two little black ears, then a pair of bright eyes peering from the long grass. The little Dexter calf sprung to its feet and started to run. We had to hurry after it to catch it, and only managed to round it up when it got caught in the brambles. It was fit and well, in prime health.

There was no possible explanation other than the deer had been suckling it. A calf can survive for a day or two, but it would have been very weak and gaunt if it had not been fed at all in this time, and the most likely outcome is that it would have died. We guessed the doe had milk because her own fawn had died. There's plenty of evidence that deer feed other orphaned fawns in their herd, and it's well known that inter-species feeding can go on. The internet has lots of videos of dogs suckling kittens and cats suckling puppies, as well as more rare examples of a dog feeding two orphaned Siberian tigers – and even a dog suckling a Vietnamese pot-bellied pig. There's also documented evidence of a tigress feeding two piglets, and a cat feeding a squirrel cub, as well as other unusual cross-species pairings. It seems that human beings are not the only ones who respond emotionally to an animal in distress; other animals are willing to offer a helping hand – or teat – when needed.

So although we could never prove it, we were sure that the doe had saved Miracle, and that's how she got her name. We got her back to the farmyard and reunited her with her mother, Marmite, who happily resumed her maternal duties, feeding her as if nothing had happened.

We don't have Dexters anymore, which in some ways is a shame as they were often the cause of special moments on the farm. One day we discovered that some of our Iron Age piglets, Tamworths crossed with wild boar, were feeding cheerfully from one of our Dexter cows. On the Farm Park we have twenty-five paddocks, and in each we have more than one species, so horses with sheep, goats with sheep, cows with pigs and so on. These piglets were big enough to reach up to the udders of the short Dexter. One of the staff noticed what was going on and I went see it. It was an amazing sight, but the cow didn't seem to mind, and I guess the sow was glad to have a bit of help ... So if Miracle was nurtured by a deer, now the Dexters were paying forward the favour.

We don't keep Dexters now because there are other breeds that are rare and need preserving, plus they're known to be lively and could be a bit troublesome. When we house our cattle for the winter they all mix together happily. As Dexters were the smallest breed, you'd imagine that if anyone was going to be bullied it would be them, but perhaps they have a bit of a Napoleon Complex because they went out of their way to assert themselves, bullying the other, more placid, animals!

Luckily Miracle and his mother Marmite weren't so bold, because when Johnny from *Animal Magic* and his production team heard the story of Miracle's survival, they asked Dad to bring the calf and its mum along. My sister Lolo went with him, and the crew asked if she would hold the calf on the set, which was tricked out to look like a farmyard. While Lolo held Miracle, Dad held her mother, Marmite. Dexters are not the most docile animals, but luckily Marmite was calm and even Miracle, who was a wild little thing at first, didn't seem to mind the lights and the heat in the studio. Lolo was not so lucky, as the heat made her feel faint. She told Dad just before they were going live on air that she was going to pass out, so Dad gave both the ropes, for Miracle and her mother, to Johnny, and whisked Lolo behind some scenery. He was back in front of the cameras just in time to do the interview although, as he said later, Johnny Morris would probably have carried on voicing Miracle and her mother as they told their own stories . . .

It was the heat of the studio that got to Lolo, but I'd lost consciousness in a more dramatic way earlier that year. Dad was trying to catch a Hebridean ram – a breed with four horns – because he needed to treat its eye infection. I was, as usual, helping out. Dad grabbed the rump of the ram and hung on, and as the ram struggled to get free it pivoted around. Thud! It caught me in the head and knocked me out cold. Dad had to release the ram and, just like in a cowboy film, filled a bucket of water from the trough and threw it over me. I came to, spluttering, and was sent to Mum in the farmhouse – soaking wet and with a large black eye beginning to appear – where I got more sympathetic care.

I wasn't put off helping Dad, and a few days later, as I was following him around to feed the sheep, I remember asking him how he seemed to know when a sheep needed extra winter food rations. He took my hand and guided it on to the back of a nearby ewe.

'I feel her back, like this. If she's too skinny, she'll

struggle to give birth, especially if she's carrying twins. Here, have a feel.'

The docile ewe let me probe her body with my small fingers. 'Good lad,' Dad said. From around this age, these sorts of moments with Dad made it clear to me I wanted to be a farmer.

A week before Christmas, it was time to sort out the turkey for Christmas dinner. I'm so glad it didn't go completely out of fashion as it threatened to do in Georgian times, when it was side-lined by wealthy families, who preferred to eat beef or venison on the big day, or even goose. Turkey was so popular that it was regarded as a Christmas meal for 'ordinary' families, and the way you showed off your higher status was to look down your nose at it. In that case, I'm very happy to be counted as ordinary, as for me it wouldn't be Christmas dinner without it. (It was also the lower classes who introduced vegetables to the Christmas feast, originally to fill everyone up on cheaper food. It's another development I'm very grateful for, because I love them all!)

We have never farmed turkeys commercially at Bemborough, but Dad used to either hatch some eggs, or buy between twenty and twenty-five turkey chicks every year for our friends and family, as well as for our own Christmas feast. They came to us in June or July and were reared in sheds until they were ready to be slaughtered and plucked. Dad and Uncle John would dispatch them quickly and humanely. As farmers, and as the children of farmers, we accepted the rhythm of lovingly caring for livestock, and then equally accepting that feeding humans was the ultimate aim, and this involves slaughter.

Turkeys have to be plucked while they are still warm, so that the feathers come out more easily. It was all hands on deck, and we children were expected to do our bit in the turkey sheds. The breast feathers came out easily, but we were taught not to take big handfuls, as this could tear the skin, which could lead to a telling off. Instead, small amounts were pinched between the thumb and forefinger. The wing and tail feathers were much more difficult, and until we were older and stronger Dad would have to take over. The floor of the shed was covered in white feathers, which we played in as if it was snow.

The birds were hung by their feet so that the blood ran to their necks, which makes better quality meat. With chickens, you can process them straight away, but turkeys are a game bird and need to be hung for a day or so, to set the meat and allow it to mature. Then Dad would bring them into the kitchen to dress them, which meant taking the grain out of the gizzards, and saving the heart, liver and neck as giblets, to be used for making stock.

A gruesome game that kept us occupied for hours at this stage was when the birds' feet were removed, and the long tendons were pulled out of their legs using a special sort of metal pliers. We children would take the feet and clench the claw by pulling on the remains of the tendons which were poking out. We chased each other around with the feet, contracting and opening them – which may sound gross but was honestly normal fun for farm children!

One year while we plucked, Dad told us a story, which may be apocryphal, about two elderly spinster ladies in the Cotswolds who kept a turkey for their Christmas meal, feeding it up in the same way that we did. After slaughtering it, plucking it and hanging it, they went to the turkey shed the following day to discover the bird, flapping and struggling upside down; it had not been properly killed, just stunned. Taking it down, they felt so upset by its plight that they could not bring themselves to kill it, and kept it as a pet. They knitted a sweater for it, because having plucked out the feathers, the bird had no protection from the weather, and he apparently gobbled around their yard for the rest of his days.

Knitting sweaters for birds is not as bizarre as it sounds; I've heard lots of similar stories in the years since. Rescue chickens often have no feathers, having plucked their own out as a response to poor, over-crowded battery conditions, which thankfully are now outlawed in the UK (but not in other countries across the world). Without feathers they are in the same state as the old ladies' turkey, and until their own feathers regrow, rescuers provide them with home-knitted sweaters to keep out the cold. Keeping up with fashion, some of the chicken outerwear is now made from fleece, which prevents the birds from pulling at loose ends of the wool.

By this time, Dad had announced it was time I had my own rare breed to look after. I was very excited by this. Dad had already involved my sisters in his rare breeds work; my sisters were all given breeds of sheep: Louise was given Shetlands, Libby had Cotswolds and Becca had Kerry Hills. For me he selected Exmoor ponies. Dad allowed us to think we chose the breeds ourselves, but I think he cleverly nudged us where he wanted us to go.

To keep us involved Dad took us to sales, and if one of our breed went under the hammer we split the proceeds with him, half for the upkeep and half for our piggy banks. It gave us all a tremendous sense of being part of the survival of these endangered animals.

I loved the look of my Exmoor ponies, and the more I came to know about them, the more my affection for them grew. They are short, stocky ponies with a thick winter coat, just the right size for a small boy to relate to.

Exmoors have a very long pedigree, right back to prehistoric times. Their ancestors roamed Europe when woolly mammoths and sabre-toothed tigers were around. These wild horses originated in Alaska and made their way to Britain about 130,000 years ago. For Stone Age man, they were a prime source of meat and skins for clothing; this hunting, plus climate change, meant that they took refuge on open mountain and moorland areas, and consequently their numbers dwindled.

The Celts started domesticating them, using hill ponies to pull chariots. In the Domesday Book of 1086 there's a record of a herd on Exmoor, which at the time was a hunting ground for the king, which offered them some protection. From then on, the area was administered by a long line of Wardens, who charged fees for grazing livestock, including ponies, on Exmoor. Gradually the different herds were established, but the bloodline has been kept very clear. Attempts to 'improve' it by mixing Exmoors with other breeds has largely failed, and these sturdy little fellas would be easily recognised by a Stone Age hunter or a Celtic warrior, because they have changed very little.

Since 1921, the Exmoor Pony Society has protected the breed, but during and after the Second World War numbers were hugely depleted – partly by people poaching them for food, owners being away at war, and trigger-happy troops training on Exmoor using them for target practice. Their meat was known locally as 'taffety', which means 'delicate on the tongue' in old Devonshire dialect.

Sadly, there were only about fifty left by the end of the war. Then a wonderful woman called Mary Etherington stepped in. She'd been left a small herd by her mother, and she rallied the other herd owners to make the moor secure, by improving the cattle grids and repairing the gates and fences. She took her little herd of twenty ponies on a train to Edinburgh, where she knew the Veterinary School at the university were looking into the conservation and protection of rare breeds like her ponies. It was a good move for the ponies and for her personal life, as she married the Professor of Anatomy who was involved with the project, and she set up a pony trekking enterprise which still goes on today.

When she called together the other breeders on Exmoor, she said something that really sums up my dad's attitude to rare breeds, and speaks for all of us involved in conservation: 'The coming generations will have good reason to call us unfaithful stewards if when we are gone there are no little horses on Exmoor.'

Luckily, there were enough others who shared her vision, and the herds have grown, but they are still an endangered breed. There are about 350 roaming Exmoor, and an estimated 3,500 worldwide.

We got our first two Exmoors from a local farmer who had initially opposed Dad's idea of the Farm Park, but came round to the view that preserving rare breeds was important. He donated two, and then Dad got a few more from Ronnie Wallace, a legendary huntsman and owner of the Anchor herd, one of the largest on Exmoor, with about eighty ponies on the moor. At the Farm Park we have always had a small herd, so in terms of going to market with Dad to sell the foals, I wasn't kept too busy.

What Dad and I didn't know then was that, decades later, I'd be filming for *Countryfile* with Ronnie's son

David and daughter-in-law Emma, who now own and run the herd. In 2013 I joined them for the annual gathering of the ponies. Teams of volunteers on horses, quad bikes or on foot bring the ponies off the moor for a stocktake, to take the foals away from their dams to wean them, check them over to make sure they are healthy, and to have them inspected by the Exmoor Pony Society, and microchipped. It was an amazing experience, and despite the heavy rain and swirling fog I'll never forget the sound of hooves drumming across the moor as they drew closer to me, the ground almost shaking when, with the older mares leading the way, a stream of dripping wet, dark brown ponies trotted past. Of course, there are always a few who don't go the right way, and that's where we volunteer herders came in.

The wild weather on that wintry day underlined for me why these ponies are so hardy, and so adapted to life in difficult conditions. They are designed for it. They have small, thick ears which retain heat (larger horses lose heat through their pricked ears) they have pronounced eyebrows and a ridge of flesh around their eyes, which is known as 'toad eye', and which keeps snow or rain out of their eyes. In the summer their coat is fine and glossy, but in winter they have coarse guard hairs on top, above a downy, insulating layer. They are so well insulated that they have 'snow thatching' in winter, when the snow that falls on them does not melt because the heat they generate is sealed under their coats. They stand in all weathers, a coating of snow on their backs until they shake it off. The shape of their tails fans out, again so that snow and rain run off. They are so good at surviving. If you watch them feeding on gorse, they carefully bite off the ends, then twist it around in their mouths so that the spikes of the thorns don't get into their tongues while they chew it.

They are sure-footed, as their natural habitat is rough ground, and their hooves are so hard that they never need to be shod, unless they are being used to regularly trot along roads. They are strong. We will never know whether Queen Boudicca's chariot really had long knives protruding from the wheels, but it was more than likely pulled by hill ponies like Exmoors.

Nowadays, growing in popularity for riding, they can easily carry adults up to 12 stone in weight, despite their small stature. They make good second ponies; in other words, they may be too strong physically for an absolute beginner at riding, but they are perfect for anyone who wants a small horse and has some riding skill.

I still have a herd today and we keep them semi-feral, monitoring them and stepping in with vet care when necessary, but in the main allowing them complete freedom to graze an area of the farm called Barton Bushes, which is designated by Natural England as a Site of Special Scientific Interest. This is because it plays host to a rare butterfly, the Duke of Burgundy fritillary, and a rare plant, the Cotswold Pennycress, which has a small, pretty white flower in the autumn. The ponies graze the land sensitively, feeding on the rough scrub and thorny bushes, opening the land up for rare flora and fauna to survive. I love the idea that one rare breed, the ponies, are helping out other rare species.

We have foals born into the herd most years, and whenever we need a new stallion we borrow one through the Exmoor Pony Society, who find us a good match for our bloodline.

I love still being involved with these special ponies which Dad chose for me all that time ago over Christmas, although sheep were my first love when I was growing up. Nowadays I have other favourites too, and one is Highland cattle. Even though they aren't endangered, we have hung onto a small herd of them. I love the look of them so much, and so do our farm visitors, that we are happy to keep them. They look great in winter, their shaggy coats showing up against a frosting of white on the fields. They stay outside in winter because with their thick winter coats they cope very well, but tend to sweat if you bring them into a warm shed. We move the few we have to an area of scrubby bush where they continue to feed without making a mess.

Highland cattle come in many colours: red, yellow, brindle, dun, white, silver and black. The popularity of the red, gingery colour that is so familiar now on all the postcards and tea towels came about when Queen Victoria announced it was her favourite, so from then on it was bred to be the largest colour group, but the original colour was black.

Mating two different colours together does not

guarantee what shade the calf will be, although there is a complicated system of genetic mapping which can predict it. It's easier to just wait and see, I think. When our cow Roseanna gave birth to her calf Valerie, she did it with a full gallery of visitors to the Farm Park looking on, which must have made their day out memorable. The tiny calf had a black father and a ginger mother, and at first appeared to be black. As she has grown, she has turned gingery. Roseanna's sister Ruby had her first calf by the same bull, and he is a chocolate colour.

Every four years or so we have to replace our bull, because by then his daughters will be coming into the herd and we need a fresh genetic line. I've enjoyed choosing bulls, and *Countryfile* viewers have followed me in my quest.

I was filmed going to Scotland for the Oban National Highland Cattles Society sales, with a budget in mind for the purchase of a new bull. Duncan, who runs the business side of the farm, keeps on top of our finances and he told me that I had between £1,500 and £1,800 to spend, so I joined the auction with that figure in the back of my mind. When I clapped eyes on Eric, a magnificent, blond bull that had won second prize in the Senior Bull category, I knew he was the one for me. He was pale yellow, with horns that turned up at the end, and he was huge. I know that expert breeders prefer smaller size bulls, because the traditional crofters in the Scottish highlands and islands would not have wanted huge animals, which are expensive to feed. Breeding to increase size has made the cattle look more commercial, bigger and meatier, which goes against everything I believe in, which is to maintain ancient breeds as they should look.

By falling in love with Eric I discarded all the sensible advice about size, and at the same time Duncan's words on the budget went out of my head as I found myself bidding higher and higher. I got him in the end for £2,500, which I justified to Duncan by saying, 'He'll be a star. We'll breed from him, the visitors will love him, then in three or four years we'll sell him on for good money to another breeder.' Duncan laughed.

Well, he did give us some good calves, and he was a hit with visitors as well as the *Countryfile* viewers. Eric was a bit of a television personality, having featured on *Countryfile* so often, and, besides, he was a magnificent-looking beast. He even had a bronze sculpture made of him by renowned sculptor Nick Bibby, who asked if he could model him. So he partly fulfilled my claims . . .

Incidentally, over Christmas of the year I bought him, 2011, he managed to lose his nose ring, and the cameras followed me as we manoeuvred his great bulk into the cattle crush, a strongly built metal cage with his head poking out, designed to prevent him hurting himself – and us. It held him while I put clamps around his neck and slid a new ring in. The hole in the nose is just like a pierced ear, and he did not feel anything.

But as for selling him on to another breeder, that idea went out of the window when Eric became infertile.

He'd had a bit of a head banger with a White Park bull which had escaped and got into Eric's field, and they faced off to each other like a couple of strutting males. It's possible that his nether regions were damaged in the confrontation, or it could be because he was later diagnosed with Infectious Bovine Rhinotracheitis, which can affect reproduction. By then he had moved to my sister Louise's farm about six miles down the road, where she kept a few steers. Once we knew about this horrible life-limiting disease, we had no choice but to let him go.

4

Christmas Abroad

You don't have to go to agricultural college to become a farmer, but I wanted to go because I knew it would give a good grounding in the skills and knowledge I needed to take on Dad's farm and legacy, and he and Mum encouraged me. Apart from learning how to run the business, they also wanted me to experience life away from my beloved Bemborough.

While I was there, I met my version of Uncle John: the good friend who'd go on to be my business partner, Duncan. We didn't really get to know each other until about halfway through the course, mainly because we were billeted in different accommodation. But then we started bumping into each other at parties, and we were both keen rugby players. Rugby has opened a few doors for me in my life, but none more valuable than my friendship with Duncan, which has never faltered in all the years since, and all the problems we have faced together. I knew straight away that he was going to be a good friend; we shared a sense of humour, and he was by nature generous and kind. He is always busy, never stops, and he has a fantastic business mind, paying great attention to detail – our personalities and talents complement each other.

In our final year at college we shared a house, and that turned out to be very beneficial for me as he organised a revision schedule and made me stick to it. I've always been interested in farming as an active job; I can happily get up at the crack of dawn to attend to animals or help out with harvesting, and, since *Countryfile*, for travel and filming. I'll work all day without a break if I have to. But I'm not at my best faced with a textbook . . .

Sitting together in the pub over well-deserved pints when our revision sessions were over, Duncan and I dreamed up a plan to go travelling for a year after college. Lots of students go abroad before or after their college and university studies, and we felt we had deserved a break – though we knew we would have to pack a lot of work into our travels to earn it.

After both getting good results (to my parents' delight) there were no objections to me taking a year out. Mum and Dad both felt I needed to experience other environments and to be sure in my own mind that I wanted to work at Bemborough for the rest of my life. I *was* sure, but I also wanted the chance to see how the rest of the world looks, and to have a big adventure before settling down.

That was how I ended up spending my first Christmas away from my family, in Katanning in Australia. Our first stop in Australia had been Perth, where we'd worked with a shearing gang. A shepherd who had worked for Dad at Bemborough, and who came originally from Northumberland, was running it and he was happy to give us roustabout jobs, warning us that the work was hard, the hours long, but the beer tasted even better after a hard day. He was right, but there were evenings when we were too exhausted even to go to the pub with the shearers.

Roustabouts don't do the skilled jobs of shearing or the grading of the fleeces by quality, but we soon discovered we did everything else. We had to pick up the fleeces, roll them and clear up, as well as helping get the sheep into the hands of these expert shearers. It was exhausting work. We travelled from farm to farm with the gang, but I didn't have much chance to see Australian farming methods, apart from making my first acquaintance with kelpie dogs, a very talented breed who help the shepherds push the sheep into the right pens.

It was one of the shearers who fixed up a good deal for us; we bought a fifteen-year-old car, a Ford Falcon XB (it's a bit of a monster, only ever made in Australia for three years in the early '70s) for 500 Australian dollars. It looked flash enough for two young men to drive around in, and it gave us good service considering the way we thrashed it.

It was that car that took us to the Dewars' farm in Katanning, a small town (over here it would be nothing more than a village, with only about 3,000 people living there) about two hours' drive from Perth. The temperature was up in the 40s during the day, and even at night rarely dropped below 20 degrees. My job was drenching – administering a liquid worm treatment to – 16,000 sheep. To an English farmer, that's a massive number, and the work was impossible during the hottest part of the day, so I worked long into the evenings. Duncan worked long hours, too, but at least he was in the air-conditioned cab of a huge combine harvester, harvesting the farm's crops.

I didn't dream about counting sheep, I dreamed about drenching them ... I did it for six weeks, through that heat, plagued by flies, to give the worm treatment to all those sheep. I had a kelpie assigned to me by Bob, and I could not have managed the job without him.

Suddenly, Christmas came around. We weren't as aware of it as we usually would have been in Britain. We rarely visited the town to pick up provisions, as the farmer's wife would take our order with her when she went shopping. So if Katanning was festooned with Christmas lights and decorations, I can't say. And certainly, in our shack, there was no sense of the festive season being upon us – I think we had both lost track of the dates, especially as the farming year over there is naturally upside down to ours, with harvest time in December.

So it was a great treat when the farmer, Mr Dewar, invited us to spend Christmas with his family at their holiday home in Busselton. It was only for a few days, but it was a real break for us after twelve weeks of long, hard work.

Busselton is a popular tourist destination, and also popular with farmers who work in the intense heat all year round, because it is noticeably cooler. Still hot by our standards, but not the unbearable heat of Katanning.

The Dewars had a large house there, with a mobile home in the grounds which Duncan and I stayed in. It was a very sociable time, because we met up with some college mates who were also working their way around Australia; the Dewar family, with lots of cousins and other relatives there, along with their two sons, made us feel very welcome. One of the most important things I brought back from my time in Australia and New Zealand was an appreciation of how open, welcoming and friendly people were, with no innate suspicion of strangers, and how they effortlessly made us feel at home. It's an attitude I have tried to take with me, because a cheerful welcome is a great gift to give someone.

On Christmas morning we headed down to the white sands of the long beach. The surfing community at Busselton, or Busso as they called it, was well established and there were plenty of bronzed, long-haired youths trying to catch waves, even on Christmas Day, and showing up the Brit novices. Luckily for us there was no wind and the sea was flat, so although we didn't get to practise surfing, at least we weren't shown up by all the experts.

Christmas dinner for us was a meat pie in a bar, with a few ice cold beers. There were no Christmas presents of course, but we did toast each other a Merry Christmas. Despite the heat, for many Australian families' Christmas dinner was a traditional roast turkey and all the trimmings; it seemed strange to be eating like that in those temperatures. I think nowadays they are more likely to be barbecuing steaks and prawns, but in those days many Australian households stuck to the British traditions: roast turkey, followed by a huge Christmas pudding that was duly engulfed in brandy flames, and the large trifle, and mince pies to follow, were the norm. They had crackers too, which a lot of Aussies referred to as Christmas bonbons, with paper hats and the usual terrible jokes.

After our very non-traditional Christmas meal we finally headed to the phone box. I'd been too busy since we'd arrived in Australia to be homesick – though of course I missed all my family and my friends. But Christmas was different. I had never been away from home at Christmas before, and even though we had enjoyed an amazing morning in the clear turquoise sea, I hadn't been able to completely switch off thoughts of Bemborough Farm, with Mum busying over the traditional meal and Dad, when he wasn't out seeing to the animals, pouring convivial glasses of sherry for everyone who was there.

There is an eight-hour time difference, so it was 4 p.m. in Busselton and 8 a.m. in the UK when we rang home, feeding coins in. It was easy enough making the connection, although the line was a bit crackly. This was long before mobile phones, FaceTime, internet cafes, video links and everything we have today, so our contacts with home had been a bit hit and miss at times when we were working far from phone boxes. Looking back, when I think how interconnected the world is today, I am in awe of my parents who cheerfully waved me off on my adventures, believing I needed to see some of the world before I made up my mind to settle to life on the farm. Mum and Dad had to make do with postcards and occasional phone calls – if they had any worries, they didn't show them.

It was Dad who picked up, probably the phone in their bedroom, and he quickly handed it to Mum, who was anxious to hear from me. She managed to hold it together while we talked; I wanted to know exactly what was going on and the familiar routines of Christmas Day back there. Dad took over, bringing me up to date on the animals and in particular giving me a bulletin about Nita, who was by now an old girl.

The time passed very quickly, as the coinbox was gobbling up my change, and the others were waiting for their turn. Dad told me later that Mum, who had sounded cheerful and normal while she chatted with me, had a few tears after the call was over. Her youngest child, her only son, was a long way from home, and not due to return for months, and it was hard for her, especially on a day like Christmas Day. I'd been at that Christmas table all my life – even when I wasn't living in the house I'd never been more than a couple of hours' drive away. Now I was on the other side of the world.

We walked back to the car in silence, engrossed in thoughts of the Christmases we were missing.

After Katanning, our next job in Australia was on a tea plantation in Queensland, which we naively thought would be easier work than the heavy labour of the last two jobs. How wrong we were. It was a horrible job in horrible conditions. You can only plant tea in wet conditions, and our job was to crawl along the rows 'gapping up', planting a new bush where one had failed, with rain constantly falling and finding its way into our clothes, however well-protected we thought we were. It was the most miserable job I've ever done, and made worse by a South African foreman who would tell us off for joking and talking.

We longed for the rain to stop, but there's an old expression about being careful about what you wish for, because when the sun shone we were put on rock picking, clearing the ground of rocks and boulders, which was serious manual labour. Looking back I can see it was character building, but it was hard to believe that at the time . . .

We lived in a mobile home about six to eight miles

away, and at night we crashed out, exhausted, too tired to do anything more than compare blisters and struggle to dry out our clothes. I look back and realise that there were people we were working with for whom this was their life, a full-time job, and we were only doing it for three weeks to raise some money. I take my hat off to them; it was a terrible existence.

The last job we did in Australia was on an arable farm in New South Wales, which was another 'character-building' experience. We were doing seed planting, and again we were working in awful, rainy conditions. Sometimes the ground was so wet it was impossible to drive even their tractors, which were the biggest I had ever seen. Trying to work the ground with these monster machines meant they sunk into the ground, or 'bogged' as the locals said. Then we had to help with another tractor, or possibly two, to drag it out.

The land flooded, and we were living in a little wooden bungalow with a tin roof. As the water rose, the mice who lived in the fields all ran for higher ground, which meant our shack. They were everywhere. We could hear them on the roof, we saw them around us – we could catch them in traps without using bait, there were so many. I opened the fridge and found a mouse in there. The whole place stank of mice wee.

Our job was to use a scarification machine to prepare the land, uprooting weeds, for seed planting. Because of the weather, and the number of times the tractors bogged, the farmer eventually brought in a plane to spray weed killer. The plane landed on the main road, filled up with spray, and then flew across the fields. Duncan and I had to stand at either end of the vast field waving flags. When the plane had flown over, spraying us as well as the field, we had to pace out fifty metres and then line up again, waving our flags, so that the plane could make another pass. Health and safety didn't get a look in, and I dread to think how much spray we inhaled.

We had packed lunches every day, because we were miles from our shack. The field was so wet that we had to eat standing up, and we were under constant attack from some big, stripy mosquitoes, which could bite you through your shirt.

When we'd finished working there we had to wait for a dry spell to escape. But although the rain had stopped the land was still very wet, and as we drove off we had to get through a ford to cross a river. I got out to see Duncan through, and at one point the car was actually floating, and I had visions of losing both Duncan and the Falcon down the river. Luckily, our trusty old car found some traction and managed to pull out.

Our stay in Australia was over, and in Sydney we said goodbye to the Falcon, with gratitude to it for seeing us through some hairy journeys. To our surprise, we were able to sell it for only a little less than we bought it for, so that still ranks as one of the best investments ever, especially when we compare it with its successor.

There were other travels still to come – including New Zealand, where a farmer whose phone number we had been given, John Cameron, hooked us up with a job pruning kiwis and gave us beds for the night, which turned into a month. We bonded over rugby, and we ended up playing for his local team. He became such a good friend that in the years since, he and his family have been over to stay with us at the farm, and Mum and Dad went out to meet his parents, who also came to stay at Bemborough.

But when the year was up, and after a brief stay in the USA and Canada, it was time to come home. We learnt a great deal on our travels, expanded our horizons and picked up ideas to bring back to the farm. For me, and I think also for Duncan, our year out confirmed that we wanted to live and work in England, and it would not be too long before Duncan joined me as my business partner at Bemborough Farm, following the model set by Dad and Uncle John. We had relied heavily on each other during our adventures, and it gave us a really good grounding for working together for the rest of our lives.

Among the many things we experienced were different types of management. While we were working abroad we were at the bottom of the employment hierarchy – roustabouts, casual labourers – and we experienced different kinds of bosses, mostly good but some bad. It taught me to always think of the other person's perspective, to be empathetic, to treat people fairly and know they will repay you with fair work.

I'd also learned how different farming could be in other countries. The Australians have such large farms that they can have flocks of 16–20,000 sheep, and many of the flock will be castrated wethers, or male sheep, bred entirely for their wool. Their fleece is very fine and makes the valuable merino wool, in contrast with our flocks where fleeces today have little value. They are shorn once a year, and they live on sparse vegetation. The arable farming we saw is very similar to ours: wheat, barley, carrots. With such high temperatures and some poor soils, the yields are much lower than ours.

Through the years I've found it's useful to watch how other cultures farm, to see if we can bring any of those learnings into our own farming practices. I've seen farmers at work in Switzerland, where every winter they have to prepare for ten feet of snow engulfing their farms. The farms are small, supported by the other jobs the farmers all have, with as few as half a dozen sheep or cattle, which spend the summers mingling with their neighbours' animals on the mountains. Then they come down to handling centres, where each owner sorts out his own. I've helped bring Valais Blacknose sheep and Hérens cattle down from the mountains for the winter, where the farmers will keep them indoors, often in sheds underneath their own homes, to protect them from snow, and with all the fodder stored to keep the animals fed until spring. This puts our Cotswold snow drifts into perspective!

*

It was a fun homecoming returning from abroad. Mum and Dad met me at the airport and of course they had not changed at all – Dad still in his familiar tweed jacket and his cap on his head, Mum as smart as ever, both grinning widely. As soon as we got home Dad rushed me out to see the new shed they had erected at the Farm Park, for the lambing demonstrations. They had written to me in Australia about the plans, which gave more undercover space for visitors, who had previously watched the lambing in a tent.

Uncle Nicky also came down to say hello, with his new wife, Marguerite Porter (Nicky and Una split because 'Wicked Uncle Nicky', as he became fondly known, was a bit of a philanderer ...), who was very beautiful, dainty, and looked out of place in a farmyard. She was a principal dancer at the Royal Ballet, and later a choreographer. She had to tread carefully around the farm, because she could not afford to twist an ankle while she was appearing in major ballet productions.

Uncle Nicky asked me all about my trip and was interested to learn how serious I was at stepping up to help Dad with the running of the Farm Park. Things were going well for him too – I think he'd just done some filming for *Inspector Morse*, though he always joked that whatever he appeared in, his epitaph would be, 'Here lies Nicky Henson – he was in one episode of *Fawlty Towers*.'

But my favourite reunion was with Nita. When Duncan and I headed off she was already quite elderly, but it was only when I returned that I noticed a big difference in her. She was fourteen, a very good age for a springer. Her legs were stiff and arthritic, she had grey hairs around her muzzle, her coat was dull and her eyes were cloudy. But oh, how wonderful it was for me to put my face into the fur around her neck again. Our reunion was ecstatic, and she attached herself to my side like the old days, following me around the farmyard at a slower, plodding pace, but with her tail wagging as enthusiastically as ever.

She could no longer tackle the stairs and was content with her bed in the kitchen, but greeted me enthusiastically every morning. I can never prove it, of course, but I sincerely believe that she knew I would come back, and kept herself going to wait for me. Her time was due, and three weeks after I came home, she died peacefully, in her sleep, the happiest end any dog could have. Nita was, and always will be, very special to me, because she was the first of the many dogs I have owned, and the most devoted, the kindest and the best dog ever.

5

Changing Christmases

The Christmas of 1991 was particularly snowy – it came down suddenly and fiercely and the farm and surroundings were engulfed, with drifts up to six feet deep along the farm track. There was the usual big, jolly gathering at Bemborough. That year Dad had invited some friends to stay, and one of them had a serious medical condition which meant he needed to take medication every day. He hadn't reckoned with being snowed in and was running out of his vital drugs. A phone call to the cottage hospital in Bourton-on-the-Water meant the medication was available and could be picked up, but the problem was the six-mile distance between the farm and the hospital. The snow ploughs and gritters had not been along our small country lanes and the snow was far too deep for normal vehicles.

We had an old Case tractor with a loader on front with a bucket attached, and so with my friend Jam we set off to dig our way out. It was a slow process, as we'd get a bucket full of snow, back up, tip it to one side, then go for another one. In parts the drifts were shallower and we were able to burst our way through like a snow plough. It took us nearly a whole day, but we did it! We were able to pick up the vital medication and drive back rather faster.

We heard later that our efforts enabled an ambulance to get through to one of the cottages near the farm, where they needed medical help, so it was a good day's work.

That was the Christmas Pete spent with us. When I was travelling in Australia with Duncan and we worked on the Dewar family farm we said to their son, Pete Dewar, the usual thing: 'If you are ever in the UK, look us up ...'

One day, the phone rang in the bungalow at Bemborough Farm. It was where the livestock manager lived – and as I now *was* the livestock manager, I'd taken it over with two friends of mine: Jam (James Collett, who ran his family garage) and Tim Lanfear, who was a firefighter.

Down the phone came a strong Aussie accent: 'G'day, Adam. I'm at Moreton-in-Marsh railway station ...'

Pete moved into a very tiny box room in the bungalow, and fitted in easily to our rough and ready bachelor life (we called that bungalow 'the squat', which gives you a general idea of what it looked like, and because we always had people staying, especially after rugby on Saturdays). He stayed for about four months, helping out on the farm sometimes, but then taking on a piecework harvesting sprouts by hand on a farm in the Vale of Evesham. We have never grown sprouts on the farm, which I'm glad about because I have never fancied harvesting them. It is hard, seasonal work, and although most sprouts are now harvested by machine, there is still a fair amount of hand picking done each year.

Pete stuck at it, but he was inexperienced, and the other pickers had been doing it for years. Their hands were hardened to stripping the sprouts off the frozen stalks, but Pete's were cut to ribbons, despite gloves, and he never made very much money. I think his lasting memory of the UK will be those bitterly cold days in the sprout fields. And that's why I am very glad we *buy* our Christmas dinner sprouts! We get them from a Vale of Evesham supplier, which means they have not travelled far.

Their ancestors travelled, though. We like to think of Brussels sprouts as one of our native vegetables, but the clue is in the name: 'Brussels'. It was not until the late eighteenth century that sprouts were brought into the UK from Belgium, and from then on we've been growing our own, with such a good supply we're now a net exporter. But Belgium was not the original country of origin of the humble sprout: they are native to Afghanistan, Iraq and Pakistan. They were brought to Europe in the thirteenth century and adapted to our cooler climate exceptionally well. We Brits can claim some ownership, though, because we eat more sprouts per head of population than any other European country.

Another veg that's an import to the Christmas table is, of course, the potato. I love them so I give thanks to Sir Francis Drake who, according to legend, first brought them to England from America. History buffs will correct me and say it was a man called Thomas Harriott, but everyone agrees it was during the reign of Queen Elizabeth I, and the story of Drake presenting one to the baffled queen is the one I like to believe.

Here in the UK we each eat about 100 kilos of potatoes a year, or approximately 500 potatoes, and I'm definitely at the top end of that average. We don't grow them as a commercial crop at Bemborough because our soil isn't suitable, but in the past few years we have been growing a field of them at the Cotswold Farm Park. We grow Red Desiree, a reliable, disease-resistant crop, good for mashing. The aim is to help people – mainly children, but adults too – understand just where the food on their plate comes from. It saddens me that city dwellers may not think any further than the supermarket in terms of where the food originates, so at our potato patch visitors can take a fork and dig up their own spuds. I was collecting a few to take back to the farmhouse recently when I met three young girls, in their late teens, who announced they had come for some potatoes. They were wearing white trainers and one of them had white jeans on, even though it was a miserable, drizzly day. I gave them paper bags, a fork and a wheelbarrow. A couple of minutes later they called to me that they couldn't see any, so I explained they had to dig for them. One of them whooped with delight and knelt down on the ground shouting 'I've found one,' as if it was the Holy Grail. They had no idea that spuds grew underground.

Our commercial crops at Bemborough are wheat, for bread; winter barley for malting for beer; oil seed rape; beans for animal feed; and spring barley, which is for malting for whisky. The crops are planted by the end of October. Dad always said that the wheat should be in before 15 October, which was his birthday, and then the beans and other crops could go in a bit later. The arable fields then lie dormant from November to February, which leaves time for maintenance of the machinery, fencing, and any other repairs needed. It's a quiet time for arable farmers, many of whom take their holidays in winter.

By the time I came back from Australia, I was certain I wanted to take over running of the farm one day, and the plan crystallised when our landlords proposed increasing our acreage.

'But we need to know that you're committed to staying on this farm, even after your father retires,' they said to me at one of our regular meetings.

'Yes, I'm definitely staying,' I replied, and Dad gave me a big grin. I don't think he had ever doubted my commitment to the farm, but he and Mum were both keen for me to not feel pressurised into it. For me, there was never a doubt; it was what I wanted to do. I think he knew it, but he was happy to hear me say it.

My sisters have chosen different routes in life, but all stay very connected to the land. Lolo has her own smallholding up the road from me, with some sheep, but she works for the Forest Peoples Programme, a human rights organisation working with indigenous peoples across the world to secure their right to their land and their livelihoods. Libby, my eldest sister, moved to America for a while, working as executive director for the American Minor Breeds Conservancy. She's an expert on rare breeds, and has helped with the breeding programme at the Farm Park. She's such an expert that she's been consulted by the UN and has been on government committees. Nowadays she lives with her family in Devon, and is co-director and co-founder of Grassroots, an online registry providing specialist software for 130 pedigree breed societies. I consult her whenever I have a breeding question.

My youngest sister Becca worked in television for many years, and now lives with her family in the North-East where they have 200 acres for sheep in Northumberland. She and her husband set up and run a charity called Useful Vision, to support blind and visually impaired children and their families, following the tragic death of their son Ben who had a brain tumour that left him blind. I am very proud to be patron of their charity.

We have always been a very close family. Becca teases me that when she broke the news to me that she was getting married, I burst into tears!

Anyway, I'd brought back to the farm a few new-fangled ideas from my trip in Australia. One of the reasons Dad was a brilliant farmer was because he knew it was worth giving something a go if it promised benefits, so he was only too happy to let me try things out – unless he'd already done so in the past and knew it wasn't worth it.

One of these ideas was introducing kelpies. There has always been a distinction, in my life and in the lives of most working shepherds, between family pets and working dogs. I don't love them any less; some of the greatest bonds I have formed have been with the sheepdogs who sleep in the kennels outside in the farm-yard. But they are not pets, they love working and they know that's what they are there for. They have such a long, proud pedigree. However automated the farm is, however high-tech our management of the land, there is one aspect of life at Bemborough Farm which has roots stretching right back to the Iron Age, when working dogs helped people domesticate animals and establish farms. When I am using one of my dogs to collect and move sheep, I am following a way of life that is thousands of years old.

I have had a succession of collies: Fen, Maud, Pearl and currently Peg and Gwen. At fourteen Peg is now an old lady and losing her sight, but still very happy to go out for walks and sniff her way round the familiar yard. I knew I needed a new dog in 2022, and so I spoke to a husband and wife team in Wales who are brilliant trainers. I had a demanding list of requirements for my new sheepdog:

I needed a bitch. All the dogs on the farm are bitches, and mixing a male dog with them could have unforeseen results, and would mean we would all have to be on our toes around them.

She needed a nice temperament because when we are filming we are often asked to do the same thing over and over until the crew have the right shots.

She must be friendly with people, because of all the visitors to the Farm Park.

Good with other dogs is vital, because of the others that live here.

Good at the job goes without saying, so she needed to be well trained.

She could not be a dog only prepared to work with one person: Luke New works with her when I am away filming or otherwise not available, and she needs to work for both of us.

It is a lot of boxes to tick, a really big ask, but they said they had just the bitch for me in Gwen. There was only one big problem: the language barrier. The husband and wife in question spoke Welsh and German, so naturally those were the languages they'd used to teach Gwen commands in. Needless to say, I don't speak German or Welsh . . .

The breeders very generously allowed me to take her on a one-month trial, to see if we could master communicating with each other. To my delight, she quickly picked up all her commands in English, she gets on well with Peg and they work together happily, she loves Luke and all of us, she goes out for walks with Charlie, she goes into her kennel easily. Brilliant.

We filmed me choosing her for *Countryfile*, but because I wasn't sure I would keep her at first, it wasn't broadcast until she had passed her month's trial with flying colours, and she's now a busy and happy member of our team at the farm. Gwen's eager greeting every morning, especially if she can sense that we are off to work with the sheep, always lifts my spirits.

The dogs work just as hard in the winter as the rest of the year. They help move the sheep around in the fields where they are feeding on turnips, and whenever I am out checking the flock the dogs are by my side. The only quiet time in their year is spring, when the sheep are in for lambing, and we make a point of taking them out for a good run every day.

The kelpies were just as special to me as the collies have been. They were the breed of dogs I had worked with handling sheep in Australia, and I was very taken with how hard-working and intelligent they were.

There were a few breeders in the UK, and I spotted an ad for a new litter in Hampshire. I chose a small, red-coloured bitch and called her Bundy (I'd drunk quite a bit of Australian Bundaberg rum out in Oz). She was an excellent 'yard dog': in Australia kelpies are not used like collies in the fields for rounding up sheep, but are brilliant at getting them into pens and loading them onto transport.

I had a couple of litters from Bundy – one on purpose through buying frozen kelpie semen from Australia (yes, really), and one by accident. I didn't know until she gave birth that the intruder was a collie, and we had a huge litter of twelve perfect puppies. The vet warned me she would not be able to cope with feeding them all and he recommended keeping six to eight, and to have the others put down.

I just couldn't do it, and in the end Bundy coped with her huge brood, with a little bit of help from me and Charlie.

Charlie and I had had a bit of an on-off relationship when we were growing up; she'd been my girlfriend when we were doing our A levels, and then we'd gone our separate ways to college. Charlie had studied photography, and then moved to London to work in TV post-production, a job she really enjoyed. We'd kept in touch and I was always secretly keen on her, but we'd both had other relationships.

Then one weekend Charlie had come to stay in one of the now empty bedrooms at the bungalow, as my mates had both moved out to get on with their lives in a more civilised way. She arranged to stay in order to go to the funeral of a family friend. We immediately clicked, laughing, chatting and getting closer. Charlie is beautiful, strong and independent. It didn't take me long to realise that I wanted to be with her. Luckily for me, she felt the same way.

In the run-up to one of the first Christmases Charlie and I spent together, I gave her a taste of what life on the farm might be like: I put a sleepy pup on her lap and gave her a pipette. She was a bit surprised because she'd been invited over for a date night, but twelve pups is a lot for one mother to feed on her own, and we had to help out!

One of those tiny pups stayed with us on the farm, and we called her Ronnie. Little did we know then that Charlie and I would go on to have pups of our own, Ella and Alfie, and that Ronnie would be the first dog they knew. She was a lovely first dog for them, affectionate, patient and protective.

Mum and Dad had always been in favour of me settling down with Charlie, although when we first got back together she was a vegan, and I don't think Mum had the slightest idea what that meant. The first meal she cooked for Charlie was a cheese soufflé which, because it does not involve meat, she thought was OK. At the time Charlie had not eaten any dairy products for some time . . .

On another occasion Mum served us avocado with prawns in aspic, and for Charlie she simply removed the prawns, with no idea that aspic is made from meat stock. Poor Charlie had to discreetly scrape it off on to the side of the plate.

Mum loved Charlie, and always included her with my sisters as if she was another daughter. That first Christmas Charlie spent at the farm after moving into the bungalow, Mum bought all four of them leather jackets from a stall in Moreton-in-Marsh market, again not realising that as a vegan, Charlie didn't wear leather. On top of that, the leather had not been properly cured and smelt of dead fish! And they'd been dyed in rather strange colours. I remember biting my lip to try to stop myself from laughing as we sat there in the living room on Christmas morning, but Charlie has always been very honest. She quickly confessed to Mum: 'I'm so sorry, Gill, but I'll never wear it . . .'

Mum wasn't offended, and said she'd arranged with the market trader to return the jackets if necessary. But Charlie wondered if by getting in first my sisters had to pretend to like theirs, which made her feel a bit guilty.

After present-opening, the feast and the Queen's Speech, it was of course time for games. I'd prepared Charlie for charades and she survived it . . . but the following year she said, 'I'm not spending Christmas with you if you're going to make me play charades.' Fair enough.

Charlie is no longer vegan but is vegetarian, which at first seems strange considering she is married to a farmer who breeds sheep and cattle for meat. Ella, our daughter, is also vegetarian, but Alfie, our son, and I are big meat eaters. Charlie is happy to cook meat for those who want it, she simply chooses not to eat it, which leads to some really grown-up conversations around farming systems and animal welfare. Charlie will occasionally challenge me about how we are managing certain animals, and it's good to hear another voice. I've always had the greatest respect for her views.

I believe that as farmers our job is to provide food that people want to eat. One of the mistakes in agriculture is producing stuff, taking it to market, and then complaining when we don't get enough money for it, perhaps because the market is flooded with cheaper produce from other countries. In any other business market research would be carried out first to find out what people want, a business plan would then work out what they would pay for it, and only then would production go ahead. We can't tell people what to buy.

If the number of vegetarians and vegans grows, then we will have to adapt to producing more goods for them. We can still feed the meat eaters. I am very sympathetic to farmers who are keen to preserve their livestock, because I feel the same way, and I love to see farm fields with sheep and cattle. But I also believe we have to live in the real world, and if that changes, we must also change.

Looking back on those bungalow days, they were a sort of 'in between' time. Childhood was over, and I thought then that I was an adult already, but really proper adulthood with all its wonders – and worries – hadn't quite kicked in. I'll admit I did catch myself thinking a couple of times how strange it was to no longer be opening stockings Mum had left us at the end of the bed, but change can be a wonderful thing too, and Charlie and I would soon be building our own family Christmases.

6

Hard Winters

Nowadays, an average winter at Bemborough and the Farm Park goes like this:

In November the cattle and pigs come into the barns, although if the weather is unusually mild they will stay out a couple of weeks longer. Every day we feed them with silage, and replenish their straw when needed. The pigs get pignuts every day. This routine carries on until spring, when the weather is warm enough to take them back to the fields. We hope to have them out by March, but if the weather is very wet they may stay in until April.

In January, as the Farm Park is closed from New Year for six weeks, the maintenance staff are also flat out making sure everything in the Farm Park is in perfect condition for opening in February – not always easy in cold, wet weather.

As I've said, when it comes to sheep, we'll leave them out and move them around the fields – closest to the farm so we can easily get to them in the case of bad weather.

One of our main jobs at this time of year is also ensuring they're well-looked after ready for lambing in spring. Around Christmas, our commercial flock of Lleyn cross Romsey ewes are scanned to tell us how many lambs they are expecting, and it's from these results that we plan their nutrition for the coming weeks.

They are pregnant for around five months, and clearly the more lambs they have inside them, the more demands there are on their bodies for food. The scanner comes to the flock, which is about 700 strong, and as he calls out we put a paint-spray dot on the side of the sheep to show which group they are in: red for the those expecting one lamb, blue for twins, green for triplets and very occasionally orange for quads. We also assess their fitness by feeling their backbone and vertebrae, as Dad showed me when I was a child, and if one is noticeably skinny we'll mark her down for extra rations. In older ewes, there's a risk that if they are underweight it can lead to twin lamb disease – this is when their bodies struggle to take in enough energy from food and they use their own fat reserves for their lambs. We can cure this with additives, and with an experienced eye it's reasonably easy to spot a sick ewe; a sure sign is when she is off her food or not as active as she should be. We can then give a high-energy drench for a few days, which gives her system a boost until her appetite improves and she begins to feel well again – if it's not treated we can lose the ewe and her lambs. We also have to check ewes are not overweight, because if they are they will find it harder to give birth, so it's reduced rations for them.

Seventy-five per cent of a lamb's growth comes in the last six to eight weeks of the pregnancy, which is why the scan at around Christmas time is so crucial, and why the carefully balanced nutrition from then on is so important. Lambing at Bemborough starts about the second week in February, and we have some late lambing ewes giving birth in April.

Winter is a time when things can go wrong for farmers. Snow can cause all sorts of issues, as already mentioned, but other problems we face include frozen water pipes. In a really cold snap a few years ago we had to leave the water running constantly because the minute we turned it off, it froze.

One of the most turbulent times I've faced wasn't a single winter, but a sustained period of years – from the late nineties into the early noughties.

In 1998, the time inevitably came for me to take over the farm from Dad. Uncle John felt it was time to retire, and Mum and Dad were inevitably getting older; the demands of the farm were heavier, and we needed to expand and do some things differently. Farming in so many ways does not change – especially livestock farming – but modern developments come along all the time, and although Dad had always been willing to look at new ways of doing things, he could see that the farm needed to move on, and he and Mum deserved the chance to take more time off.

They had already started offloading a lot of the responsibilities for running the farm on to me, and I'm the first to admit I wasn't the best at working out the finances, nor had I really got my head around the arable side of things. The Farm Park was expanding; the shop needed more stock; the café was booming which meant employing more people ... I needed help, like Dad had needed Uncle John.

'Never imagine you can do everything, Adam,' Dad told me. 'A lot of the skill in farming is getting the right other people involved, you can't be an expert at everything.'

I knew immediately that Duncan was the one person I really wanted to work with. He has a more businesslike brain than mine, and he understands arable farming. We get on so well, and after our year-long travels I knew we would always be able to work together. I could see a future for us on the same model that Dad and Uncle John had.

He came to Bemborough originally as farm manager, but always in the knowledge that after the handover from Dad and Uncle John, he would be my partner. It has worked really well ever since, through bad times and good.

Handing over to the next generation is always a tricky time for farmers, but it's one that inevitably has to happen with family farms. I think we managed the takeover as well as possible, but it had its awkward moments.

In 1998 Charlie was pregnant with our daughter Ella.

We hadn't married and didn't feel the need to: after all, Dad had been born 'out of wedlock', as they used to say, and we regarded the birth of our baby as the greatest commitment we could make to each other. We are both independent people, but we knew from the moment we got together – and even more so when Charlie became pregnant – that we were making a lifelong pledge to each other and our children.

At the same time, Dad's aunt Benita died, and she left everything she had to Dad. Benita (this was the aunt after whom I named my spaniel Nita all those years ago) was a real character, the sister of Dad's father, a physiotherapist by training who had been a WREN (the Women's Royal Navy Services) during the Second World War. She had moved to live near to us, in the village of Guiting Power, lived well into her nineties, and attributed her good health to having a cold bath at the start of every day. When she was in hospital with her final illness she was sitting up in bed reading *Les Misérables* in the original French. She told Dad she'd had a good life and didn't want it prolonging unnecessarily, but she had a phobia about being buried alive, and made him promise he'd make sure she was really dead before she was nailed inside her coffin!

When Dad inherited her home and everything else she owned, it meant that he and Mum had enough money to buy a house in Bourton-on-the-Water, about five miles away from Bemborough Farm. He did not need to take any money out of the farm business for the move, which was just as well as we were running on a large overdraft. We were lucky; I know how hard it is for a lot of family farms to move from one generation to another.

The terms of the tenancy dictated that the tenant had to live in the farmhouse, which made sense because Charlie and I were expanding our family, but to us it felt as if we were intruding on my parents' territory. It was really tricky for Mum; she had spent thirty-six years bringing up her children there, nursing her parents and Dad's mum there in the end stages of their lives. Because they moved into a smaller house, many of their belongings and furniture remained at the farm, which made it even more difficult to think of it as no longer theirs. Mum would walk in and go straight to a cupboard to look for something she thought should be there, to find it had been moved – or even got rid of altogether.

Dad came to the farm most days, and he would walk into the kitchen without knocking, perhaps with a feed merchant in tow, while Charlie was breastfeeding Ella at the kitchen table.

'Any chance of a coffee, Charlie?' he'd say, breezily.

I think this transition is something that affects all farms that are handed down through the generations. Charlie was very patient, but in the end I had a quiet word with Dad about knocking before he came in, and gradually both Mum and Dad came to accept that the farmhouse was ours, and that we would live there in our own way.

We never moved into their bedroom though, even

though it's the one with an ensuite. That would have felt too weird . . .

Duncan and I were only a couple of years into running the farm when 2001 swung around, a big year in many ways. After a lot of heart-searching, we had borrowed quite heavily to bring the Farm Park up to date, and to make it a better attraction for school trips and other visitors, and we were looking forward to earning some of our investment back.

Then, in February, we got the news: foot and mouth disease had been detected at an abattoir in Essex, the first outbreak for many years. Foot and mouth is a highly infectious disease that, without control, runs rampant through sheep, cattle, goats and pigs. The only method of control is culling the animals.

The previous outbreak, in 1967, must have been worrying, but I was only a year old so I don't have memories of it. It mainly affected northern areas of the country, but it must have been a worry for Dad, who had only been farming at Bemborough for five years – and for all farmers of livestock the worry has never completely gone away, as the disease is always prevalent somewhere in Europe.

The outbreak of 2001 was different from those earlier ones. It caused a massive crisis in agriculture and tourism – and to plenty of other people besides. Moorland, common land, river and canal banks were all off limits. Dog walkers, particularly those who did not have gardens to exercise their pets, found it hard to get out for walks except along roads, and horse owners had to exercise in restricted fields.

For us, it was much closer to home than the 1967 outbreak; having started in Northumberland it quickly spread to Essex and Buckinghamshire, partly because in the intervening years, with the closure of many abattoirs, there was more movement of animals around the country. In no time at all there were cases in Devon, North Wales, Cornwall and then the Lake District.

Over six million cows and sheep were killed to try to stop the spread, and in parts of the country the stench of their bodies being burned on pyres made farmers weep openly. Farmers may breed livestock for market, but that does not mean we don't care deeply about our animals, and not just as a business asset. We take the care of living creatures very seriously, and with very few exceptions farmers work hard to make sure they are well nurtured and looked after.

I told Dad: 'If it gets to us, you and Mum must go and stay with Uncle Nicky in London.' I couldn't bear the thought of him watching his life's work destroyed. Thank God, this never happened.

Our farm was in the middle of a restricted area and we had to stop access to all except the most vital visitors. The smell of disinfectant hung in the air, as everyone had to walk through troughs of it every time they entered or left the farmyard. We couldn't take any stock to market, as they were all shut, and we couldn't sell directly from the farm. No animals could be moved.

The policy brought in by the government was that all animals within a three-kilometre radius of an infected animal had to be culled, so every day we were scanning the news to see where the latest outbreak was, just hoping it wasn't close enough to mean the worst day of any farmer's life: watching his healthy stock being taken away to be slaughtered and burned. The nearest outbreaks to us were, luckily, about thirty miles away, so we escaped the cull. The government was later criticised for the severity of the cull, with so many healthy animals being killed. In Gloucestershire, our county, seventy-one farms were suspected of having the virus, and later tests showed that only thirteen were actually infected, but that was too late for 15,000 cattle, 59,000 sheep and 1,080 pigs slaughtered in this county alone.

This all happened within a very short space of time – the epidemic only lasted a few weeks – although there were restrictions on animal movements for a year, and that whole summer was a total nightmare for us and other farmers.

I remember Duncan and I sitting at the kitchen table in the farmhouse, contemplating what to do next, as I'd seen Dad and Uncle John do many times before. I knew we were capable, but I worried we weren't experienced enough to get us through the crisis unscathed. Duncan and I are both very practical, pragmatic people, but there were times when we could not see the end in sight. All our assets were tied up in the animals and the farm equipment, and our income had simply evaporated. We had to close the Farm Park, which was terrible timing given our expansion plans. Then, as now, we lived in rented houses: although our lovely farmhouse is a real family home, it is part of our tenancy so we don't own it. We genuinely thought we might lose the business and our homes. It was a devastating time and not just for farmers like us; all rural businesses suffered: pubs, youth hostels, hotels, everyone with a stake in the countryside.

We were saved by an insurance policy, which Dad had very wisely advised us to keep going; thankfully, we weathered the storm. Our staff on both the farm and at the Farm Park were magnificent. They simply said: if you can't afford to pay us, don't worry. Some of them offered to look after the rare breeds without pay, because they cared for the welfare of the animals as much as we did. We even received unsolicited donations from members of the public who had enjoyed visiting the park and were worried we would be unable to afford animal feed. Their generosity was humbling.

We lost about £100,000, so although we didn't feel lucky at the time, I can look back and see that it could have been worse, and compared to many farmers we came through relatively unscathed. We lost no animals, and we benefited afterwards from an extra influx of visitors because people wanted to get into the countryside again – and we were very pleased to see them.

It was a wake-up call for me and Duncan about our precarious personal positions, and as soon as we were earning enough we each took some money out of the business to buy ourselves houses. We rent them out, but it's comforting to know that we have them as a fall-back, and as something to show for all our years of hard work.

It seems that farming will never be completely free of epidemics. We cope with regular TB testing of our cows, and there is no more worrying time for a farmer than waiting for the vet to ring with the results. A positive test means losing a cow; depending on the size of the farm and the herd, this can be a very serious financial loss, even though there is compensation paid. Every year across the country we lose about 23,000 cattle to TB, and it's something we all fear.

In a way, I'm glad Duncan and I had to contend with something so huge right at the start of our farming careers – it gave us the confidence we needed to know we could overcome the inevitable challenges faced by farmers. It also cemented our relationship – I can't imagine having gone through that crisis without Duncan to share all the pressure and worry – and, I think, made it clear to Dad just how well-equipped we were to look after the farm in the future.

After all this, the Christmas of 2002 was a special one. We'd come through some very turbulent years and to top it all off, it was the first Christmas we spent as a family of four – my daughter Ella was four and my son Alfie was seven months old. I remember looking back on what we'd achieved and enjoying the fruits of our labour – quite literally too, as every year we make sloe gin and vodka (the latter being for Charlie, as she doesn't like gin). We'd picked the sloes back in October. As there were so many blackberries growing in our hedgerows, we'd also made blackberry gin, following the same methods Mum had taught me: for every pound of the fruit use half a pound of sugar and half a pint of gin. There's an old saying that you shouldn't pick your sloes until after the first frost, as this softens the skin and helps release the juices, but with the climate so variable nowadays, it's not necessary to wait that long – we pick our blackberries and sloes in early autumn, or whenever they are clearly ripe. If you pick before a frost, you can prick each berry with a pin and put them in the freezer, which works just as well as frost.

I don't know which vintage we were drinking – we've always got some sloe gin or vodka maturing in a corner of the dining room, under the drinks cupboard. We make a batch each year for consumption the following year, so that it has matured well – the trick is to remember to turn it, especially for the first few weeks. But I do know Charlie and I were sitting in the living room with glasses in hand at the end of Christmas Day, with both of our babies asleep upstairs. How strange that we were now the parents!

Mum and Dad were the best grandparents we could have asked for. Mum, especially, loved the idea that the farmhouse where she brought up her children now had another generation of little ones to trail mud across the kitchen floor, and that there were more children to marvel at the lights on the tree and the magic of Father Christmas visiting us.

When Charlie resumed her career and I was busy working, Mum was a great help with childcare. She and Dad enjoyed their retirement, carrying on with their entertaining, and making the most of the time to travel. But it was great to know that, whenever I needed it, I could give Dad a call and he'd come down to the farm in his tweed, cap firmly on his head, rubbing his hands together and ready to help out.

7

The Christmas Cat

Nowadays, commercial turkey farms transport their birds around the country by road, but for centuries farmers had to walk their flocks to market, often for many miles. As many as 250,000 turkeys were walked to the Leadenhall meat and poultry market in London from the late sixteenth-century forerunner to Smithfield Market, in time for Christmas, often from great distances. The Norfolk turkeys travelled over 100 miles, and some came from even further afield, setting off as early as August so that they could have plenty of stops for food and rest on the way – nobody wants to buy a skinny turkey.

To protect their feet, small leather boots were fitted, and making turkey boots was a good sideline for cobblers and shoemakers. Geese, who were also walked all the way to market, refused to wear the boots, so instead they were herded through warm tar, which stuck to their feet, and then sand, to give them a good, protective layer. There's an old country expression for anything that is impossible to do: 'to shoe a goose'.

The drovers who took the birds were, in modern terms, freelance; London buyers, or buyers from other big cities and towns, travelled around the country buying up flocks, then employing the drovers and their dogs for the long journey to the market. In the run up to one Christmas I demonstrated this ancient way of life for *Countryfile*, taking forty geese for three days across the Brecon Beacons in Wales to the market town of Llandovery. Obviously we couldn't walk them through tar – today this would not be approved by animal welfare experts, and we made sure we had a vet on hand to check them over at the end of each day. It was hard work, especially in the bleak and wintry weather conditions on the hills, and I was glad I was only doing it for three days. One night I slept in a tent and had to make do with the drovers' rations of dry bread, cheese and a raw onion, with my dog Maud cuddled up to me for warmth. Even this was a luxury for a drover, who would have slept under hedges or, if they were lucky, in barns. They relied on their dogs to alert them to foxes and even rustlers stealing their livestock.

I also had the benefit of a long waterproof coat and a hat with a brim, while they would, at best, have had woollen coats which would have been sodden and heavy, and impossible to dry out. Dad used to go out in all weathers in a tweed jacket; the smell of wet tweed, steaming by the stove in the kitchen, is nostalgic for me, but I would hate to give up my waterproofs.

One of my geese seemed to be struggling with the

walk more than the others. The others preened their feathers to get rid of mud, but she stayed bedraggled and was lagging behind. I called her Jemima, after Jemima Puddle-Duck, the Beatrix Potter character, and I carried her for part of the walk. I was worried, but when the vet joined us he said she was fit enough to continue. I know that the old drovers accepted that a few of their large flock would not make those months-long treks, and I heard they had the occasional unexpected early Christmas feast along the way, when a goose died.

I was following one of the ancient drovers' tracks which criss-cross the landscape, avoiding roads used by carts and carriages because of the turnpikes, where drovers had to pay for every animal, even a goose, which waddled through. Every few miles we stopped to give our geese a rest, so progress was slow. I was exhausted when we finished our trek, but pleased to report I did not lose any of my geese, and they were all in good condition, even Jemima.

Taking such a slow route to market gave me time to reflect on how fast we expect to do everything today, when the geese would simply be loaded into trailers and delivered within hours. To some extent I am a fan of the old traditions, but this is an instance of when I would not like to go back to the old ways, and I'm full of admiration for the men who took on such a difficult job, just to make sure everyone had a plump fowl on their table on Christmas Day.

For another *Countryfile* programme, Ellie Harrison and I decided to have a race to see who could get our flock to market faster, Ellie with twelve geese and me with the same number of turkeys. Apparently this was an old challenge that farmers set each other, often with a wager on the outcome. In the early 1700s two lords had a huge bet – 100 guineas which would be worth more than £12,000 today – on the long walk to London, and the geese won by two days. Despite knowing this, I still thought I was onto a winner, as turkeys are bigger, stronger and have longer legs, and we were only covering a mile and a half.

I was joined in Team Turkey by James and Pat Peel, who farm turkeys, and Pat warned me that the birds could be 'a bit lively' for us. He was right. Turkeys are more wayward than geese, and mine had a habit of deciding to roost in trees and bushes. We walked through pouring rain, and after a spell struggling to keep them all going in the same direction, I cheated by loading them into the back of a trailer. I was determined I was going to win, by fair means or foul. Unfortunately, Ellie felt just as competitive, and her flock of geese also hitched a lift in a trailer.

After my skulduggery I was certain of victory, but I was outsmarted by Ellie and her geese. They weren't entirely well behaved, but they were a lot more disciplined than my turkeys. Ellie wound me up by pretending to still be struggling when I rang her as we approached our destination – the village green in

Banham, Norfolk, so I was genuinely surprised to see her there ahead of us.

Cattle and sheep also had to be walked to market until railways made transportation easier in the first half of the nineteenth century, but they still faced long walks to the rail stations. That's why local fatstock markets were very popular, and the Christmas market, traditionally held in the last week of November or first week of December, is still a landmark in the calendar of cattle breeders. At the market, prizes are awarded for the best livestock, with the emphasis entirely on the meat quality. The buyers judge the depth and thickness of the hind quarters, the fullness of the loins and the thickness of flesh over the shoulder. It's not a beauty competition.

After the morning's shows, an auction in the afternoon sees local butchers competing to buy the best animals; they then proudly display in their windows the rosettes awarded to the livestock they've bought, to show customers how good their meat is. Some butchers still follow the tradition today. It's heartening that UK supermarkets are now buying all their beef from British farms.

There was a very well attended Christmas fatstock sale in December 1894 at Windsor, when cattle belonging to Queen Victoria were auctioned. Such was the demand that carriages were hired to meet the trains at Windsor station and ferry buyers to the sale in the castle grounds. Everyone wanted a piece of royal beef.

Anyway, because I'd been so busy driving geese and

filming other programmes for *Countryfile*, I was cutting it fine with Charlie's Christmas present. Like a lot of men I can rely on Charlie to organise presents for everyone. Sometimes I go Christmas shopping with her, but if I am too busy she takes it all on. She is brilliant at it, knowing exactly the right thing for everyone.

There's one person Charlie can't organise a present for though, and that's Charlie herself. That year I did not have any ideas, and I didn't have any time to get to the shops to look for some.

Then inspiration struck. I was filming on a farm where there was a semi-feral cat with kittens, all spilling around the farmyard.

In the big dog-versus-cat debate, I come down firmly on the side of dog, and the only cat we'd ever had was Percy, a beautiful (but diabolical) feline, half Burmese, who belonged to Charlie before we got together. Percy confirmed all my prejudices about cats, being vocal (a high-pitched meow) and arrogant enough to refuse to go outside when he needed a pee. Percy's wet patches, and the smell of them, became a normal feature of life. He even expressed his distaste about the arrival of our first baby, Ella, by peeing all over the brand-new car seat I had bought to bring my newborn daughter home from hospital. There was definitely no love lost between me and Percy; I'm convinced he was jealous of Charlie having someone else in her life as well as him, and he was on a mission to get rid of me. But I knew Charlie adored him, so I bit my tongue and put up with him (although I once asked the vet – who'd come up to the farm for one of the animals – how long cats lived, secretly hoping Percy's time was nearly up).

When Percy's life was finally over, I swore we would never have another cat. But now, desperate as I was for an idea for Charlie's present, these kittens seemed a good idea.

'If you can catch one you can have it,' the farmer told me.

The kittens were about three months old, and they weren't about to allow themselves to be caught by anyone. Even my best rugby tackle wouldn't have worked – they disappeared as soon as I looked at them.

'There's a queen with a litter on the top of those straw bales,' the farmer said, after enjoying my attempts to catch one. 'They're younger, but they've been weaned. If you sneak up on them it might be easier to get one.'

I climbed up the straw bales and there, on top, was the mother cat, lying in a little bed of straw with her kittens all around her. I had taken my coat off and I gently threw it over them in the hope I could then pick one up – but they bolted into the straw, apart from one little one who was left behind.

I carefully carried her down, and when I looked at her I figured out why she hadn't got away: she was sneezy and her little tummy was bloated; she was a sad spectacle. The farmer said to me, 'If you want it, take it, because it doesn't look as if it's going to survive if it stays here.'

I put her in a cardboard box and on the drive home stopped at a supermarket to buy food and other cat essentials. I was beginning to have second thoughts, remembering that like a dog, a cat is not just for Christmas but for life – probably at least fourteen years.

I'd grown up with a farmyard full of feral cats, kittens everywhere, because Uncle John loved cats, and they were effective at keeping vermin at bay. But as a sheep farmer I am now aware of the risk cats pose to livestock because they can carry toxoplasmosis, a parasitic disease that can be passed to sheep and pigs. Most modern livestock farmers use a pest controller, and cats are limited to family pets.

I gave the little kitten to Charlie when I got home, since it clearly couldn't wait for the big day as the little thing needed a lot of TLC, and I would never have managed to keep her hidden. It's fair to say Charlie had mixed feelings. Much as she loves cats, she was worried about this sad, sneezy little specimen – I'd potentially just brought home a lot of heartache for her and the kids. Luckily, our local vet Jill Allen called in that afternoon. She had become a good friend, and if she was in the area she would pop in for a coffee. Charlie showed our latest addition to her and her reaction said it all:

'Oh my God.'

She immediately went to her car and came back with wormer, flea treatment and an antibiotic jab. I think Charlie must have told her not to send the bill to me, because I was already regretting my impulse present . . .

Despite her uncertain start though, the sad little kitten grew into a beautiful, fluffy cat who was named Twiglet by the children, because her tortoiseshell colouring was the same as a twiglet, and because she was so small. She became everyone's favourite Christmas present. Alfie and Ella were six and ten by this time, just the right age for looking after another member of the household.

She soon settled into life on a farm with a kitchen full of dogs. She never peed in the house and she went a long way to converting me. I'd still choose a dog over a cat any day, but Twiglet was definitely the acceptable face of cats, and Charlie, Ella and Alfie loved her to bits. She lived a long, happy life and had two litters of adorable kittens, all of which were happily rehomed. We kept one from her last litter, Frank, and he's still with us, at the ripe old age of fourteen, and like his mother he's a great addition to the household.

Giving Charlie a cat for Christmas isn't the only time I've decided an animal would make the perfect gift. Many years later I was filming in North Wales for a Channel 5 series called *Family Farm Rescue*, talking to farmers about their plans to diversify, when I met some beautiful goats. They were Anglo-Nubians, beautifully dappled and spotted. Anglo-Nubians are a nineteenth-century breed originating from the days when P&O steamers brought goats back from exotic parts of the world like India, the Middle East and North Africa, using them during the voyage for milk and meat, then selling the remaining ones off when they reached port.

They were cross-bred with traditional British goats to make this large, lop-eared goat.

The colouring of these goats is different to our native goats and I thought they looked gorgeous. At the end of filming I couldn't resist buying three, sticking them in the back of my pick-up truck and driving them back home. It was Ella's twenty-second birthday coming up, so they made a great present – and no wrapping paper needed.

We gave them names from the Flintstones: there's Pebbles, Wilma and Bam-Bam. As Bam-Bam wasn't related to Pebbles, he fathered her first kid, Fred. We've run out of Flintstone names for all the kids that have now been born! Pebbles is a very friendly goat, and when we first had her she would come out for walks with us when we took the dogs out, at first on a lead and then just trotting at our side. The goats live at the Farm Park, and Pebbles is one of my special friends when I walk around – without fail she'll come over to say hello to me. She's so pretty that she is a great favourite with the visitors.

Ella and Alfie are now twenty-four and twenty-one, so I don't suppose I should call them children anymore, but we keep up the tradition of giving them stockings at Christmas. I'm afraid, like so many parents, we spoil our children at Christmas, and instead of the ribbed fisherman's sock I once had, Charlie cuts a pair of tights in half, through the crotch, to fill with an assortment of presents. Tights are very stretchy, and you can get a lot

122

more in there than in a ribbed sock. Charlie makes sure Ella and Alfie get the same number of stocking presents each, all wrapped in different gift wrap from the main presents, which are under the tree. That's because it's Father Christmas who fills the stockings, isn't it?

Spoiler alert if anyone under the age of about ten is reading this: when Alfie was nine or ten he had his suspicions about Father Christmas confirmed in the oddest way. He was really into wildlife, and we had given him a motion-sensor camera, one that you can set up outside and leave overnight. Movements by badgers, foxes and other nocturnal animals will trigger the sensor and record their activity. He hadn't had it long and was still experimenting with it. On Christmas Eve, Charlie and I, both giggling because we'd enjoyed a glass of wine or two (or three), tiptoed into his room to fill his stocking, checking first that he was sound asleep. It was only as we were leaving that I spotted a small light flashing in the corner of the room: he'd set up the camera in his bedroom. We were caught red-handed. I don't know whether he did it deliberately, but at least after that I didn't have to go through the biting of the carrot, much appreciated by Rudolf, and half a mince pie, left out for Santa, along with an empty brandy or sherry glass.

8

Wildlife in Winter

When Dad died in October 2015, I clipped a lock of wool from the shoulder of one of our best Cotswold sheep, and placed it in his hand, inside a coffin also made of wool. It was an old tradition he had told me about: shepherds, when they reach the Pearly Gates, can show St Peter the wool, and he will know that they were unable to get to church regularly because of their duties to their flock, and would forgive them.

Dad's death was widely mourned; Joanna Brame, the series producer for *Countryfile*, put together a very moving tribute to him which John Craven presented on the programme. The obituaries in the newspapers all recognised his importance in rare breeds conservation, and there were more very moving tributes at his funeral, led by Uncle Nicky who took the death of his older brother hard. It was a very difficult time for all of us; he had been the centre of our family for so long. We buried Dad's ashes and his favourite flat cap in the same area where all his faithful dogs have been laid to rest, surrounded by beech trees. Sometimes I go out there and find myself telling Dad what we're up to. It's a beautiful place for reflection. Even though I know he can't hear me, sometimes the wind ruffles the leaves and it feels as if he's saying something back.

It was only when Dad had gone that I fully realised how much I still valued his advice. Once Duncan and I had taken over the running of the Farm Park, he never tried to impose his views on us, but I drew on his very long experience of animals all the time. In those early days, things would crop up that I would instinctively want to ask him about – then his loss would bite again. That still happens every now and again.

I'm sure many people agree that Christmas is a strange time when you've lost a loved one. It can be a time of such joy, but for some reason this makes you reflect on sorrow and memories too. The first Christmas without Dad was especially strange, and for Mum most of all. We were all conscious of wanting to make it seem as normal as possible, for her, but aware that it could never be the same without him. Dad loved Christmas, all its traditions, he was always at the centre of it, laughing and joking. It was difficult to face it only two months after his death so it was an inspired move by my sister Becca and her husband Nick to invite us all up to the Northeast for a few days, which at least meant Mum would not have to face sitting in their beloved farmhouse feeling his loss even more acutely.

After Dad died, I noticed the robins on the farm more

than I had done before. 'When robins appear, loved ones are near' says the old country rhyme, and although I don't really go for superstitions, whenever I see a robin hopping around the garden or singing in the hedgerows, I think of Dad, and I give a nod to the bird.

There are probably more myths and legends attached to robins than any other bird, mainly because they are instantly recognisable with their bright red breasts, and they have been around for hundreds of years. In Norse legends they protected people from storms, and the Celts called them the Kings of Summer, which is not as odd as it sounds to us who associate them with winter and Christmas. In fact, they live in Britain all year round, along with half of all our birds, although we may spot them more in winter when so many leaves have fallen and branches are bare. If you are good at recognising birdsong, you will know that they sing all year round – except for a few weeks around mid-summer when they moult and lose their bright plumage. At this point they become rather shy and retiring, waiting until all their finery is restored before emerging as their usual cocky little selves again.

There are at least three Christian legends attached to the origin of their distinctive red breast. Perhaps a robin fanned the flames of the fire that was warming the baby Jesus, and scorched his breast by getting too close. Or in another version the fire was too hot, and the little bird protected the baby. Or it was a drop of Christ's blood that coloured his feathers after he plucked out a thorn on the road to Calvary. In Wales, there's a tale that the little bird was ferrying water to the parched souls in purgatory and was singed by the fires of hell.

What these legends prove is that robins have always been part of British life, and because their nature makes them unafraid around humans, we see them more than other birds. But don't be deceived by appearances: they are tough and quite prepared to fight to the death to defend their territory. In the summer you might see two together, a mating pair who will work cooperatively to see off intruders. In the winter months, they live alone.

Their role as a symbol of Christmas probably sprang from the legends surrounding the birth of Christ, but in Victorian times, when the Christmas card was invented, they shared the epithet 'redbreast' with the red-jacketed postmen who delivered the cards. They naturally became the star attraction on the cards, often with a card in their beaks, or perched on a post-box.

In stories they often feature as guides, helping lead the children in the *Chronicles of Narnia* by C. S. Lewis, and also leading the way to *The Secret Garden* in the book by Frances Hodgson Burnett. I can understand why. When one perches on the handle of my spade with his head cocked to one side I could swear he is trying to tell me something, lead me somewhere . . .

The Christmas after Dad died, when we were all in Newcastle, Charlie gave me a life-size brass robin, a lovely, thoughtful present that sits in our lounge.

*

In the run-up to the following Christmas in 2016, I was able to take part in something very special. The closeness of the sheepdog and his master is something that has always been recognised in rural communities, and that year I made a programme for *Countryfile* which featured a Christmas carol service, with the church lit up with candles and sheepdogs lying in the aisle of the church beside me.

It was customary for churches in the Scottish Borders to host special Christmas services where sheepdogs were allowed, because the church ministers recognised that otherwise the shepherds would not be able to worship. Many of these men lived solitary lives, in small cottages, tending their flocks with a faithful sheepdog their only companion. Even for a family man, the sheepdog was so important to his life and livelihood that they would spend all their days together. These dogs would follow their masters to the ends of the earth, and would not be left outside a church if their owner was inside. If the dogs could not come in, neither could the shepherds.

I joined in with the choir at Bowden Kirk, just south of Melrose in the border country, and as we rose to give full voice to 'While Shepherds Watched their Flocks by Night', the dogs stayed peaceful and quiet. This, apparently, was not the case in years gone by, when the whole service, including the carol singing, was conducted sitting down. If the shepherds stood up to sing, their dogs would also get up and start heading for the door, assuming they were off back to the hills. Apparently travelling priests, new to the area, found it strange to have dogs in church at all, and even stranger to have the whole service conducted sitting down.

The sheepdogs sprawled in the aisle next to me were very relaxed, and happily slept through the singing. It was moving to see how the special bond between shepherds and their dogs was so strong that they went everywhere together.

We spent that Christmas back at Bemborough. Late in the frosty afternoon, I pulled on a warm jacket and took the dogs out for their last walk of the day. There is nothing I like more than going out when the sun is low in the sky and the light is a faded golden colour, and looking up to see a barn owl flying low and silent up the hedgerow, quartering backwards and forwards to find small prey, then swooping with deadly precision, giving me a flash of a white underside before making off with a wriggling meal. I watch with mixed feelings: I want to see this magnificent bird catch his prey, to ensure his survival, but there's also part of me that wants to warn the little voles and mice to run and hide because a ruth-less killer is circling overhead.

I love owls, and I love the fact that the ones I see and hear today on the farm are the descendants of those same birds who sent me to sleep with their hoots as a child. They are an important symbol of the continuity of this farm, from generation to generation.

There is also something very special about being out at night when the winter air is clear and cold, and the sky is full of stars, listening to the owls calling and the foxes barking, and I especially noticed it without Dad. Nature feels more present, perhaps, when we've lost someone. Occasionally I heard the strange scream-cum-bark of a muntjac deer, the small solitary Chinese deer which has gone native in some areas of England, and which is so secretive that I only occasionally catch a glimpse of one around us.

Christmas for us humans is a time of plenty, of feasting and over-indulgence, of waistbands feeling slightly tighter than they did before the break, of putting our feet up in front of roaring fires or in centrally-heated rooms. Just one more chocolate? Another mince pie? A top up for your wine glass? Oh, go on then . . .

Those of us who live on the land like to think we are in tune with nature, but Christmas is the time of year when we are most out of sync with the world outside. As we face the over-abundance of our Christmas tables, birds and other wildlife are squaring up to the toughest time in their calendar: the Hungry Gap. That's when the nuts, seeds and berries of the autumn run out, and spring is still a few bleak months away. Frost hardens the ground, making it difficult to pull up worms or dig up roots and insects, and all the berries and seeds have been eaten. It's a tough time of year, and when the weather bites hard it is important to remember that spring always comes, that the cycle of life goes on, and in time everything will be renewed.

We've always had winters, of course. But it is only

in recent years that we have all become more aware of the damage that is happening to the environment, and to the habitat of so many of our native species. Since the Industrial Revolution we've lost over half of our biodiversity, which is a lot more than most countries in the world.

As you can tell from my devotion to preserving rare breeds, I care a great deal about conservation. I know that helping birds, butterflies and other wildlife to survive is as important as saving our Gloucestershire Old Spot pigs and Belted Galloway cattle, and all the other breeds we look after and maintain at the Farm Park. In setting up the Rare Breeds Survival Trust in 1973, my dad and his fellow enthusiasts were visionaries when it came to saving endangered British farm animals, but it has taken longer for us all to catch up with the need to keep Britain's rich and diverse nature on track.

The finger is often pointed at farmers for causing the crisis in our wildlife, and I'm not ducking the accusation. I can see that when people left the land and their smallholdings to move to work in the factories in the late eighteenth and early nineteenth centuries, it opened up the countryside to be developed by farmers on a much bigger scale. Naturally, grubbing up all the hedgerows and small vegetable patches and concentrating on certain crops meant that many birds and small animals found themselves without homes and without their regular supplies of food.

In the last 200 years these islands have lost more

than four hundred different species of birds, plants and mammals, and we have a lot more that are threatened with extinction. Since 1970, we've lost ants, bees, beetles, butterflies, dragonflies, moths, spiders, wasps, and today more than 40 per cent of our bird species are threatened with extinction. As far as mammals are concerned, there are bats, voles, dormice, hedgehogs, shrews and others that are now classified as vulnerable. Even harvest mice, those cute little fellas who were a familiar sight for my farming predecessors as they scampered away when the crops were brought in, are now at risk.

It is, of course, not just farmers. Our growing population has meant more and more land developed for housing and industrial sites, and now we have the problems of climate change, which are having even more devastating effects on our wildlife.

The good news is that we have all become more aware of the problem. One of my heroes is Sir David Attenborough; by raising public awareness of the consequences of climate change, he has made the world sit up and take notice. Whether you live in a city, or on the land like me, we are all more conscious of our duties to protect our natural world.

Our farm has been in something called the Countryside Stewardship Scheme for twenty years, which means we made a commitment to increase biodiversity and improve the habitat for wildlife on our land, which we've since upheld. One of our winter jobs is to encourage the birds and small mammals to set up homes around the edges of our fields. We plant pollen and nectar mixes for the bees, butterflies and insects, and barley, kale, lupins, peas and other plants with different size seeds. The birds can feed on them in autumn and winter.

We also buy about three tons of bird seed, which we take out to the hedgerows in sacks, then transfer it into buckets with holes in the bottom. Charlie and I, and the kids if they are home, walk along distributing it, the dogs capering along beside us, every day in the coldest times. The landscape is bare, with stark branches of trees outlined against leaden skies, and the ground under our boots is hard and unforgiving; it feels important to be lending a helping hand. During this Hungry Gap, when all the natural food is gone, the seeds we scatter help the birds survive to be fitter and fatter in spring, and more capable of rearing healthy broods of chicks.

It may be a time-consuming job, but it's very enjoyable because the birds wait for us they know where we will be dropping their food, just like birds often know when a garden bird table is going to be replenished. It's one of my great winter pleasures, a job that does not feel like work.

We also leave tussocks of grass in our fields for skylarks, who are ground-nesting birds, to protect them from carrion crows and raptors who prey on their eggs later in the year, and these patches also serve as habitat for voles and mice, which in turn provide the food for owls.

Nowadays we see blue tits, chaffinches, goldfinches, yellowhammers and many more breeds that years ago had almost disappeared from the countryside here – the variety of birds hopping about in our hedges has increased noticeably since we joined the scheme, and the birdsong, always quieter in winter, is nevertheless louder and a wonderful medley.

There are plenty of ways to help wildlife survive the worst of winters in your own garden. You can make hedgehog cover for hibernation with piles of leaves and grass cuttings, and if you buy a hedgehog house, place it in undergrowth or surround it with leaves. The best food for these little visitors is dry, meat-based cat food.

Birdfeeders are great – keep them topped up with seeds and nuts. Try to avoid any bird feed with wheat, because wheat is particularly attractive to pigeons and larger birds, who will always dominate, preventing small birds from feeding. Bird houses should be high, and position them out of direct sunlight.

If you have badger visitors, they will eat wet cat food or dog food, and foxes will devour your leftovers. But be careful not to feed wild animals so much that they become dependent on you, and so stop foraging for their own food.

The most useful thing you can do in times of deep frost is to keep a good supply of water, checking regularly that it has not frozen over. There are many good people out there who think about feeding wildlife, but not as many who remember to water them.

9

A *Countryfile* Christmas

By 2019, I had worked for *Countryfile* for nearly two decades. I had got the gig in the early noughties when the then daytime farming and rural affairs programme put a nationwide call-out for a new presenter. It never occurred to me to apply – it was Charlie who said I'd be good at it. At first I didn't take her seriously. I'd been brought up around television cameras when Dad was filming but I thought of myself as a farmer, and I was finding that job a struggle just then – it wasn't long after Duncan and I had taken the farm over and we'd had to contend with the foot and mouth crisis. That was how Charlie clinched it: 'The money would be very useful.' I couldn't disagree with her there.

With her television experience she patiently helped me make an audition tape, including some of the farm animals. To my amazement, I was then asked to spend two days with a handful of other hopefuls in Wales, going through more strenuous auditions. I spoke to Dad before I set off; 'Speak to the camera as if it's your friend,' he said. 'Just a mate you are chatting to.' It was advice that has stood me in good stead.

Eventually, after our tapes were road-tested by a sample of 100 *Countryfile* viewers, I heard that I had won, and that I would work alongside John Craven ... for one day. The opportunity had changed and the BBC no longer needed a full-time presenter. I'll admit I felt a bit cheated; but Dad told me to go along and make the most of the experience. He also gave me another piece of advice: 'You are not too good for anything. Make the tea, carry equipment. Make yourself useful. Who knows what will come from it?'

He was right – I got a whole, long-lasting career from it. Dad found it funny just how closely I ended up following in his footsteps, though Uncle Nicky also liked to think it was *his* footsteps I was following in. He was my biggest fan; after he died, his kids told me that nobody could phone him while the programme was on, and afterwards he and Dad would ring each other to talk about it. Nicky gave me sound advice about becoming a public person, and being recognised by strangers. He told me always to smile and be pleasant, however I might be feeling. It always amused him when we were together and people recognised me but not him. It was the same advice Dad gave me: 'People want to talk to you because you are in their homes; they enjoy or respect what you do. You need to look after that respect, and make time for them.' I've never found that hard; I really enjoy meeting people and talking to them.

Over the two decades since I started at *Countryfile*, quite a bit had changed for me personally and professionally, but one thing that hadn't was our annual Christmas party, which we held every year after our Christmas special was filmed. It was always a very jolly event, something none of us wanted to miss, and a chance to unwind and let our hair down with all the hard-working crew and office team whose work behind the camera is as important as ours in front of it.

But first we had to film the Christmas special. We are often working in isolation unless there's a segment to do together – like when Anita Rani joined me on the farm to help me round up the cattle. But because that's only a rare pleasure, it's nice to have a moment in the year when we'll all be in the same place.

The Christmas specials traditionally take us to stately homes and manor houses around the country which are beautifully decorated for their Christmas visitors, and make a great backdrop to our festive programmes. Other presenters tackle making wreaths and tree decorations, looking at traditional food preparation, and other activities with Christmas themes. For my part, there is always something with a farming or countryside management aspect.

That year we were filming at Tyntesfield, a large country house that is a fine example of Victorian Gothic Revival architecture in Somerset; a magnificent, ornate pale stone mansion filled with wonderful furniture and paintings. But naturally I was not inside – I was there to meet and help the farmer, Nick Green, who is tenant of the 400 acres of rolling farmland that is part of the estate. It was a familiar duty for me, helping him bring his Angus cattle into the sheds for the winter – exactly the same job I was doing at Bemborough that week with our fifty cattle of five different breeds.

As Tyntesfield is a National Trust property, Nick farms it without fertiliser, weedkiller sprays, and with grass grown in fields that could otherwise be used for crops. As we do, he too leaves habitat untouched for insects and wildlife. Grazing his cattle on the land keeps the estate parkland looking perfect.

It struck me as ironic that while Nick farms without fertiliser, the wealth of the Tyntesfield estate was founded on guano, the natural fertiliser provided by the droppings of seabirds in South America. William Gibb, who became known as 'the richest commoner in England', made his fortune importing this dried bird poo, which is a very good source of nitrogen and phosphate and was used for thousands of years by South Americans. He used his vast wealth to completely renovate and preserve the magnificent mansion. The trade in guano ended in the early twentieth century when chemists discovered how to make fertiliser in laboratories, and then factories.

Less familiar than the farmland for me was my trip to the traditional kitchen garden and the glasshouses. Manager Charlotte Langley showed me the perfect rows of sprouts, kale, celeriac, carrots and spring onions that a small army of National Trust volunteers tend under supervision, and she explained how the produce is delivered to the café at the big house twice a week, and any surplus is given to the volunteers and visitors. I was envious of the estate's orchard, which has 300 apple, pear, walnut, quince, plum, cherry and mulberry trees, somewhat eclipsing our orchard, which consists of several apple and pear trees. The old Victorian glasshouses have been restored, and in the orangery I saw, in midwinter, oranges, lemons and limes ready to be picked from the trees growing there. Figs and pineapples would have been grown here in Victorian times, too, to add an exotic touch to the Christmas table.

But the biggest treat for me was the cheese that is made from the milk of Nick's herd, and I was able to share samples of this at the round up of all the presenters at the end of the programme. John Craven, who always enjoys dressing up, was very happy to be dressed in a full Victorian costume . . .

Speaking of dressing up, it was on to the annual party, which I was hosting that year at the Farm Park. We took over the restaurant, which was decorated beautifully, and we were served a delicious traditional turkey feast: Claire Fisher, our catering manager, and her staff really did us proud. There were between thirty and forty of us, presenters and production staff, and it was our usual jolly event with plenty of liquid refreshment.

As he nearly always did, John came as Father Christmas in order to distribute all our Secret Santa gifts. He would really throw himself into the part, getting into character and giving a lot of 'Ho, Ho, Hos'. By this point in the proceedings, we'd always shared a bit of Christmas cheer, so we were well and truly in the mood for his jovial performance. Then when he'd reappear without his costume, we'd all say: 'Oh, John, you've missed Santa . . .' (One year, when John was unable to be with us for some reason, I was dragooned into filling the big black boots of the Santa costume, which I did with some trepidation because I knew I could never emulate John's complete mastery of the role.)

But this particular year there was a near-disaster during John's Santa performance, which still gives me chills just thinking about it. At the time we had some working oxen so I thought it would be a great idea to yoke a pair to a flatbed trailer, and put Santa's sack of presents on the back. One of the oxen, named Philip (they were a royal pair, with his partner named Edward) was accustomed to being ridden, so we gave John a leg up onto his back, and they set off plodding towards the restaurant, with me leading Philip and another guy holding Edward. As soon as we came into sight, lots of the presenters and crew ran out and jumped on the trailer which, in retrospect, was pretty stupid. There were no health and safety executives around at the time . . .

The oxen plodded on steadily until unfortunately a gust of wind suddenly whipped John's red Santa hat off his head, and it fell past the face of Philip the ox, who jerked, causing the trailer to jolt forward and everyone on

board to jolt too. I held Philip tight and gave him a reas-
suring 'Whoaaaa', my heart in my throat. Thankfully
nobody had fallen off the trailer and – although there
was one scary moment when I thought he might – the
ox didn't bolt with the legend that is John Craven on his
back. Had Philip bolted, Santa Claus and the whole of
Countryfile – presenters and crew – would be sprawled
in the mud, probably with quite a few casualties. It was
a narrow squeak . . .

The rest of the party I'm pleased to say went really
well, with a tour of the barns to see the animals, and
I was relieved that the full number boarded the coach
with all their limbs intact at the end of the day.

John's Christmas experience with my oxen was not
the only time one of them has given him a bit of a
fright. Some years before, we were being filmed walking along a muddy farm track with a pair of Long Horn
oxen when the one John was holding suddenly lurched
and yanked John forward. John stumbled and tripped,
falling in front of the ox, which thankfully stopped.
John sprang to his feet, laughed, and being the expert
presenter, carried on talking to camera as if nothing had
happened. My heart was in my mouth though, because
an ox of that size could seriously damage someone by
trampling on them, and if it had bolted John would have
been dragged across the field. Thankfully they are quiet
creatures, and we only ever used well-behaved pairs. At
one time we had three or four pairs of oxen, all trained
to walk together on halters. It was a nice little sideline,

as we could hire them out for events and for film work. We tried oxen from different breeds, including the ancient White Parks, Longhorns (whose dramatic horns made them a popular choice for films set in the past), Gloucesters and Welsh Blacks.

If you pay very close attention you'll see me and a college mate on screen in *Braveheart*, the Mel Gibson film, wearing ginger wigs and kilts, walking behind the actors who were leading the oxen pulling the body of the hero's father back from the battlefield, so that we were on hand if required. Although they didn't fit the period of the film perfectly (they were bred later, in the eighteenth century), they were the only working oxen in the country, so the film producer had no choice and besides, in the late thirteenth century, when William Wallace lived, cattle would have looked similar to them, with their impressive horns.

I also spent some time in London on the set of *Alien*[3], using an oxen team to pull a spaceship out of a lake. We were filming for weeks, but the whole scene was dropped. That's showbusiness for you . . .

Our oxen weren't the only film stars on the farm. We've provided pigs, one for a rather eccentric Colin Firth film called *The Hour of the Pig*, and another one for *101 Dalmatians*, for which I spent a week training a pig to sit on command. You can see her sitting on Glenn Close, who played the villain Cruella de Vil. We also provided various animals – sheep, goats, pigs, geese, cattle – for the Monty Python film *Life of Brian*, and more recently for *Robin Hood*, starring Russell Crowe.

One of the weirdest things I had to do was to get a small herd of pigs to swim so that a camera crew could film them from underwater. The film they were making was a Biblical story, about the parable of the Gadarene swine, when Jesus sent the demons that were possessing a man into a herd of pigs who ran dementedly off a cliff and into the sea. The crew had been filming in a hot country, but they needed some footage of the pigs' trotters frantically swimming under water.

Dad was friendly with Daphne Neville, who is known as the Otter Lady, and who lives in a converted water mill near Stroud, where she rescues and cares for otters. We decided the race, the channel that conducts the water to the water wheel, next to her mill would be ideal for the filming. I had no idea that pigs can swim, but I discovered they can – and they kept swimming away so fast that when I was out of my depth even my best front crawl couldn't keep up with them. It took me ages to get them back onto the bank. In the end I had to construct an underwater pen out of sheep hurdles to stop them swimming away while the cameraman captured the footage he needed.

Despite the practical problems, it was always a pleasure to use our rare breeds in these ways, helping to bring them to a wider audience. As with the White Parks, many of our animals are genuine ancient breeds, with a bloodline that goes back directly to the wild native breeds that roamed the British Isles before our ancestors in the Iron Age enclosed them and started farming instead of hunting them. Back in the 1970s, when I was eight years old and Dad's youngest but most enthusiastic farm worker, he was asked to help stock a recreation of an Iron Age village with the sort of animals that would have lived alongside the inhabitants. The village, Butser Ancient Farm, is an open-air archaeology museum in Hampshire, with recreations of Stone Age, Saxon, Celtic and Roman buildings, so that school parties, archaeology students and members of the public can see how our ancestors lived.

The sheep were easy: Soay sheep from the St Kilda islands were an obvious choice, because they survived in isolation for thousands of years, untouched by cross breeding.

We know from excavated bones that swine were an important foodstuff for our forebears, and that these primitive men kept herds of them. As no exact descendants exist, Dad borrowed a wild boar from London Zoo and mated him with two of our Tamworth sows, because Tamworths are the oldest known domesticated breed. The boar was certainly wild, and some of his piglets inherited his feisty temperament. Others were easier, and by careful breeding we created a pig that looks like a wild boar but has the calmer qualities of a domesticated pig.

Tamworths were in a real crisis as a breed in the UK, because there simply weren't enough of them to keep the line going without risking inbreeding and consequent genetic defects. Dad, on his travels for a television show in Australia, heard about a herd of Tamworths, and managed to bring three young boars back to Britain for the Rare Breeds Survival Trust. We no longer have Tamworths at the Farm Park, because they have become much more popular, so now our pigs are British Lops, lovely traditional pigs and a very rare breed.

Training oxen for the village was arduous; we had to start when they were calves, and pair them with another ox of similar size, then work with them until they were fully grown. At one time we had three working pairs, and as a feature of the Royal Bath and Wells Show we took all three teams into the show ring, with me sitting on a cart behind one pair, wearing a smock – yet again.

I was also filmed for a *Time Team* programme, one of the long series that explored the archaeology of Britain, presented by Tony Robinson. The archaeologists wanted to see how our Iron Age ancestors managed to plough their fields with oxen pulling an old wooden plough. It was very difficult, and I take my hat off to the men who did it. Oxen are not always willing to pull: if you harness a working horse it is immediately ready to work and will give you its all. Oxen have a mind of their own and, however well-trained, can be temperamental. They will stop if they feel like it, and sometimes just sit down. If you ever watch an old Western with teams of oxen pulling the wagon train, you'll see that the men driving the oxen use whips. We were never prepared to do that, so a lot of coaxing had to go on, and that's without the difficulty of trying to get a wooden plough to cut into hard ground.

Our oxen always worked in the same pairs, so when the dreaded TB struck one of them, it meant they could no longer be yoked together. You couldn't simply put them alongside another ox, not without another long spell of training, and that was the main reason we stopped using them. It was a lucrative sideline when we first did it, but eventually other animal owners got on the bandwagon and were undercutting us. For us, it was only ever an extra that we offered, and in the end it wasn't worth the work required

Do you remember Eric, the Highland bull I bought for a small fortune who sadly became infertile? His successor was Archie, and he had an illustrious pedigree. In 2014 I went up to the Balmoral Estate in Aberdeenshire, a home for the royal family since it was bought by Prince Albert for Queen Victoria in 1852, and where the late Queen Elizabeth kept a herd of Highland cattle. She introduced them to the 50,000 acre estate in 1953, the year of her Coronation, and they thrive there, ideally suited to the conditions, winning lots of prizes at shows. With the help of her stockman Dochy Ormiston, who knows everything there is to know about Highland cattle, I bought Archie, a really good-looking animal, only fourteen months old and quite small in contrast to Eric. His name was chosen by the Queen herself, so although I had originally planned to call him after Dochy, of course I couldn't change it.

Choosing names for animals is fun, and I understand why the late Queen used to enjoy naming all her farm newborns. When filming there I was privileged to see a foal being born to one of her Highland ponies; he was given the name Adam by Sylvia Ormiston, the stud manager and Dochy's wife. Apparently, when the Queen heard the name she was happy to keep it, because the theme for that year's births was Biblical. I met up with my namesake when at Balmoral for another visit and he has grown into a strong young pony, one of a sturdy breed that reminds me of my own Exmoors. Adam went on to win Best in Hand at the Royal Highland Show, a tremendous accolade, and Sylvia very proudly sent me the pictures.

I was worried Archie might not be big enough to serve our cows, but Dochy reassured me, in his broad Scottish accent: 'You try stopping him.'

He was, of course, right – one of his daughters, Ruby, is actually on the front of this book. She has a lovely temperament herself and has proved a good mum to her calves. I think she inherited her nature from Archie; he grew into a fine fellow, gentle and easy-going. I always felt relaxed around him – which I can't say for all bulls.

When I was invited to lunch with the Queen and Prince Philip a year later (yes, I'm name dropping), I was honoured to be seated next to Her Majesty, and astonished when she asked me about Archie. She met so many people, from so many walks of life, but she told me her real passions were dogs, horses and farm animals – and she remembered her bull.

Archie served us very well, but eventually, just before Christmas 2019, when his own daughters were mature enough for breeding, we had to let him go. It's part of a natural cycle for anyone who breeds animals, but particularly sad because we were all very fond of Archie. He still had good years left in him – a bull can work, siring beautiful calves, until he is ten to twelve years old – but Archie was no longer suitable for us because of the risk of inbreeding. I sold him to a very good home, a breeder just up the road from us in Stroud, and I know he has gone on to have a happy and productive life. He was a gentle soul, loved a good scratch and happy to see me when his cows were not in season. I always choose quiet, good-natured bulls because they are lovely to have around, and also because they pass their temperament onto their calves.

In spite of Archie's absence, it was a really exciting time for us. We were about to be a year away from our fiftieth anniversary of the Farm Park, and we were in full-preparation mode. We'd had a glamping site for about fifteen years, with eight luxury tents complete with log burners and fitted kitchens, and a few camping pods, which were less luxurious but fitted with bunk beds and with electricity laid on, as well as a site for camper vans and those who wanted to pitch their own tents. We were in the process of opening six new lodges which would take everything to a much more luxurious level, and would, we hoped, tempt more families to spend weekends and whole weeks at the park. They are rustic-looking wooden buildings, fitted to a high standard inside. They sleep six, and three of them have hot tubs. Obviously, they needed to have fully equipped bathrooms, so we had to provide new sewage and water supplies, as well as electricity, because our existing cesspit and our single-phase electricity would not cope. We were able to put in a new ablutions block for the campsite at the same time. It was a very expensive investment, made possible because when our landlords changed in 2017 we changed the terms of the tenancy, with the farm being on a farm business tenancy, and the Farm Park on a commercial lease. Our landlords were very supportive and enabled us to do the expansion, investing in it alongside us. We knew it was all quite ambitious, but we'd calculated it would work – it was exciting to reflect on how far we had come from that first day when Dad invited the public in to see his beloved animals.

We were also doubling the size of the restaurant, which for some time had been struggling to cope with the number of visitors, and we were also doubling the size of the shop. We are very proud of the range of goods in our shop, which include many from local sources, such as honey, oilseed rape oil, lavender products, sausages, bacon, milk and eggs. The staff had been overwhelmed by the popularity of it, and they needed more space to display goods and have better till facilities. The extension also meant that we could have offices upstairs, which made everything more civilised for our workers.

We'd also started investing in better pathways around the park, making access easier for pushchairs and wheelchairs, and drier under foot for everyone; we had also come up with plans for new animal shelters, to be erected nearer to the pathways, so that visitors could be closer to the animals. We created a sensory garden which everyone can enjoy, but which is designed to bring special pleasure for those with special needs.

One tremendous innovation, which we achieved with the help of a grant from the county council, is an adult changing room, with hoists and every facility needed for disabled adults and their carers. It's a wonderful addition, because we all care passionately that the Farm Park should be open to all, and it's our job to make it as accessible as possible.

We'd worked out our budgets very carefully, hours spent talking it through with our accountants and advisors and Duncan designing and leading the projects. As 2020 began, our maintenance manager Gavin Dowdswell and his team worked incredibly hard to make sure we could open in February, in time for school half term. And then . . .

10

The Covid Christmas

If you visit the Cotswold Farm Park at Christmas, you enter a mystical realm, especially as darkness descends across the fields. A bewitching trail of twinkling lights leads visitors through a fairy-tale world populated by real animals as well as mythical beasts. The barns, fields and woodland are illuminated, and installations tell the stories. There are firepits to warm the travellers, and along the route various places for hot drinks and snacks, and our Ox Shed restaurant and bar stay open for more sustaining food and drink. On a frosty evening, the glinting lights are reflected in every blade of grass, enhancing the feeling of entering a magical, make-believe kingdom. It's a triumph of the imagination of our creative staff to conjure up the themes, and the lighting experts who come in to do all the work setting it up.

Christmas opening at the Farm Park has only been a feature for the last five years, and it has proved to be a beguiling addition to the usual year-round programme.

Credit goes to Kate Lord, the general manager of the Farm Park, a very efficient, hard-working member of our team who is also great fun, and who came up with the idea to extend our season right up to Christmas. It is part of the evolution of the park, which is always developing and improving. In Dad's day the Farm Park closed in September; first we extended it until after the October half-term school break, and now it runs through to New Year, except for Christmas Day. The Christmas opening has proved more and more popular each year, so although those 'shoulder months' of the winter are still loss-making, at least the losses are reduced.

Of course, the revenue it generates is also invaluable, because we have the costs of keeping all our animals fed and well cared for when we are closed, as well as maintaining our 100 staff, who are very loyal and hard working. So all those excited children and their parents are not only enjoying a Christmas outing, they are helping us preserve the ancient rare breeds the park was originally set up for. What started as a hobby for my dad has become a centre for education and pleasure for thousands of people each year.

On New Year's Eve 2019, at the end of our Christmas opening period, there was a New Year's Eve party at the restaurant, which had been booked by a large party who were staying in their motorhomes. It was very busy for our staff, and since we have been opening at Christmas I have a deeper appreciation of everyone in the hospitality business and other jobs who work over the time in the calendar when the rest of the world is off, relaxing and enjoying themselves.

But soon after the start of 2020 we honestly didn't know if we would make it to another Christmas opening at the end of the year. As I've said, we went into January 2020 looking forward to celebrating our golden anniversary at the Farm Park in the following year, and were already making plans for special events to mark the anniversary.

But gradually, as the days went by, more and more news reports were talking about a coronavirus, which was spreading fast and causing unexpected deaths in China. There had been a couple of confirmed cases here in the UK at the end of January, but geographically it still seemed so far away. I remember seeing the news report about the cruise ship in Japan at the beginning of February, where all the passengers were being kept on board in quarantine – thinking how awful it was and thank god it hadn't hit us in the same way.

The realisation of just how serious the situation was took the whole nation by surprise, and the senior management team at the Farm Park spent hours talking over what was likely to happen.

At first we thought we might be able to stay open – most of the Farm Park is open air, after all, and people weren't worried about being outside. Staff still worked in close proximity to each other, however; we didn't want to put them at risk. The problem we faced, like so many other hospitality and tourist spots across the

UK, was that closing meant saying goodbye to income. And without income, how would we pay the staff? How would we feed the animals?

The decision to close was taken by three of us: Kate, the general manager of the Farm Park, Duncan and me. We sat around a table, despondently facing up to the inevitable. We would have loved to have found a way to stay open, but we had to face the stark reality. The incoming government restrictions only meant one thing: closure, and however much we tried to juggle possibilities, this had to be the outcome. Before we told the public on 19 March, we announced it to the staff, giving everyone a week's paid leave while we tried to work out where we were going. That was the scariest part – even though we knew we had to do it, we didn't have a plan for how to stay afloat. We'd borrowed heavily for the improvements. We were – to use a technical business term – overgeared, which means that, on paper, we had borrowed more than the business was worth – and Duncan and I had also invested personally. The park's spring opening was supposed to help us pay back the money we owed. Now we couldn't borrow more, and we couldn't pay back what we'd borrowed.

I made a video to explain to our customers and supporters that we were closing, and I was filmed standing in front of a field of our sheep. I'm unashamed to say that I had tears in my eyes and had to swallow hard to say the words:

'Hello, my name is Adam Henson. My business

partner Duncan Andrews and I are the tenants here at Cotswold Farm Park. The park opened in 1971, so next year is our fiftieth anniversary. Its earliest beginnings were because my dad had a passion for preserving and conserving rare animals. To pay for his expensive hobby he decided to open to the general public and tell them the story of the rare breeds and also about farming and where your food comes from. Over the years the business has developed and grown and we now get around 160,000 visitors a year, many are season ticket holders and members who come back regularly to visit us. We are really, really proud of what we have built up here, but these are terrible and difficult times, unprecedented, with Coronavirus.

'We have now taken the decision that the responsible thing to do is to close. That's very difficult for the business and for us as individuals, and also very hard for our staff. Hopefully, financially, we'll get through this.

'I don't want this to sound corny or crass, but when my dad died in 2015 I was at his bedside and I promised him I would look after this, I would look after his legacy, I would look after his rare breeds. And I am determined to carry on doing that.

'We all value your support, so thank you.'

I am very proud of the work Dad and the other original enthusiasts at the Rare Breeds Trust did, and I'm even more proud to have upheld his heritage. That's why, on that grim day when I had to announce the closure of the Farm Park to visitors, it felt as if a part of my life was being destroyed. I hoped, but was certainly not sure, that we could survive. There were many sleepless nights in store for Duncan, me, and the senior management team.

Like every other business in the hospitality and leisure section, we knew we might have to make redundancies. We simply could not afford to pay everyone their salaries while we were closed. The staff were amazing, all of them understanding what a terrible position we were in, all of them expressing concern for the park, none of them complaining about their own circumstances. In fact, they set about collecting together any spare protection equipment we had in storage – finding 800 aprons, 2,600 pairs of gloves and 120 hair nets which we donated to our local Winchcombe Medical Centre. It was a good reminder of the hard work being done by so many others to keep the country safe, both medical staff and volunteers who were looking after the vulnerable.

I know that our problems have to be looked at in context – people were losing their lives from this terrible disease. An old school friend of mine, the same age as me, went to bed one night and never woke up because of severe breathing problems caused by Covid. I had Covid once myself, but apart from being knocked sideways for a couple of days, and feeling tired for a week or so, I escaped without any complications, and I know how lucky I am.

But the truth is still that, as tenants of the land and the farm, Duncan and I were facing losing everything, not just the Farm Park. We both live in tenanted houses; we could lose our family homes, our work, everything we had built up. Then there was the staff – they all had rent and mortgages to pay, too. Most of all, we were worried sick about the animals, who don't stop needing food and care even if the whole country has shut down.

A couple of times I walked out to the clump of beech trees where Dad's ashes are buried and had a quiet word with him. I knew him well enough to recognise that he would understand the predicament we were in, and I knew he would not brand me a failure. But I *felt* a failure, I felt I was letting everyone down, even though the logical part of me was aware there was nothing I could possibly do. I was watching the news all the time, fearing the worst but hoping for a breakthrough.

Then the miracle we were praying for happened. Honestly, I don't know what we would have done without it. In March, the Chancellor of the Exchequer, Rishi Sunak, announced the introduction of something called 'furlough'. What? I had no idea what the word meant and had to look it up, and discovered it meant 'a temporary suspension from work, usually used in a military sense'. I was as baffled as most of the country, but, like every other employer, thrilled when I realised it meant that the government was prepared to pay up to 80 per cent of our staff wage bill.

It was properly called the Coronavirus Job Retention Scheme, but the word furlough became part of the English language. On the night after the announcement was made I had my first good sleep since Covid struck. The staff were safe! There was still a great deal to worry about, but one big problem had been removed. The cavalry had appeared over the hill.

My daughter Ella, who was twenty-two that spring, was another person who was placed on furlough from her job in marketing. Ella and her boyfriend Sam had actually been planning to go travelling that spring, but now the world was in lockdown they of course couldn't do that. They had to move into the farm with us, where Alfie was too, retreating from university. At least we were altogether, and we were spared most of the food shortages that hit the country. We had a supply of loo rolls from the stock of the Farm Park, and we had endless packets of biscuits and crisps that were going out of date, and plenty of pots of jam.

Strangely – although I found it hard to relax and enjoy it at the time – in hindsight, March to July was a peaceful time on the farm. The farmyard, always busy with visitors coming and going, was calmer and quieter, and inside the house, with Ella and Alfie back home, it was a special time for Charlie and me. We were able to go out for walks and appreciate the tranquillity of a countryside free from traffic, in the roads and in the air, and although I still had plenty of jobs tending to the animals and the rest of the day-to-day farm work, the number of phone calls and emails dropped off and there was more time to spend as a family. Alfie helped out on the farm, which was very welcome, and Ella was a great addition to the marketing staff in the office. Although there was a great deal for us to worry about, I never forgot how lucky we were to be living in this beautiful place, to not be cooped up and away from family during this terrible time. We have always been a strong family unit, and we never forgot to count our blessings.

There was more good news. Business rates were suspended, VAT was reduced to 5 per cent from 20 per cent, and our landlords were prepared to give us some grace on our rents. We have a very good businesslike relationship with our landlords, and they recognise that it benefits them if we thrive. I know from talking to others that not all tenant farmers had such considerate and supportive landlords. A survey by the Tenant Farmers Association found that a third struggled to pay their rents during the pandemic.

With all this good news I could walk through the trees and tell Dad that I could see a way through, that I was not going to have to disperse our animals or, even worse, slaughter them. We, and the business, were going to survive, and it was a lovely feeling.

So much of that first half of 2020 was spent problem solving, but that didn't mean the rest of our work on the farm or with the animals stopped. And in that spring, we were eagerly awaiting the birth of a Suffolk Punch foal.

Suffolk Punches are a critically endangered breed

which can be traced back to 1768, to a stallion owned by a man called Thomas Crisp, who lived, predictably, in Suffolk. We don't know what he called his horse, so history refers to him as 'Crisp's horse'. But compared to the Exmoor ponies, the Suffolks are real newbies.

I was first introduced to them by a man called Nigel Oakley, an ambassador and world-renowned breeder. We met at the Norfolk Show, where I was filming for *Countryfile*, and Nigel talked to me about his important work helping to increase the numbers of Suffolk Punches. I took to him immediately: his flat cap reminded me of Dad, and so did his down-to-earth attitude.

I instantly fell under the spell of his Suffolk horses. 'Punch' is their old name, and it was originally used for a short, stout person. It's difficult to think of this description applying to them, but I suppose compared to the other heavy horses that used to populate the farming landscape, the Shire and the Clydesdale, they are a smaller breed, while still towering over most other horses. They stand between 5ft 7in and 5ft 10in to their shoulders, and they have a strong girth, stockier than the other heavy horses, so I suppose 'stout' works.

We'd had a Suffolk on the farm before, in Dad's day, but she had been quite aggressive, which gave me a bad impression of the breed, and we didn't keep her long. Nigel persuaded me that she was a one-off, and that as a breed they are gentle and easy to train.

It was Nigel who gave me my first Suffolk, Victoria. What a great gift! She is a very popular attraction at the

Farm Park, as gentle and as eager to please as all her breed. She has what horse experts call 'a kind eye'. You can walk up to her in the field and put a collar on her, give her a pat, and she'll nuzzle your hand. Whenever I talk to her I put on a Suffolk accent, like Nigel. He always says, 'Come on, me old mate,' to his horses, so if I want her to do anything that's what I say, in my best Suffolk brogue. A hand on the bridge of her nose and another on her chest, and she backs up beautifully, without a harness. Obviously, females are important in any breeding programme, but particularly so with horses. One stallion can service many mares, but the mares can only produce foals after a long, eleven-month, pregnancy, so the more females we have, the better for the future of the breed.

Nigel had trained Victoria very well; he is my mentor and I call him whenever I want a bit of Suffolk Punch advice. His horsemanship skills and understanding of working horses are sadly disappearing, and people like Nigel are now rarer than the Suffolk Punches he loves. When I visit him, he enthusiastically talks me through his wonderful collection of harnesses and accessories.

Victoria was about thirteen years old when she came to us, and showed no inclination to breed when she was introduced to a stallion, probably feeling she was old enough to be past all that carry-on. We wanted to breed Suffolks as a way of helping out the breed, which has less than 300 breeding mares, but it was clear that Victoria wouldn't play ball and so we decided to buy a younger mare.

We picked Lexi, who was already in foal when she moved to the farm. Everyone took to her instantly because, like Victoria, she is a friendly girl – although not quite as docile, as she can be a bit of a madam at times! She settled in very quickly.

When it was time for her to deliver her foal in the spring of 2020, we sent her to Andrew Thompson, a very experienced Suffolk breeder who is a past President of the Suffolk Horse Society. I was taught early by Dad that when you need an expert you get an expert, and I'm the first to admit that I do not know how to help a mare give birth. Give me a pregnant ewe who is in difficulties and I will do all I can to help, but I'll also call a vet when I need one. Horses, especially such a precious (and large) breed as the Suffolks, are definitely not within my remit when it comes to being a midwife.

I eagerly awaited the phone call from Andrew; we were all still in the throes of the first lockdown and waiting for Lexi to become a mother was a ray of light at a dark time.

But then, when the phone finally rang, it was bad news. Very sadly, Lexi went into premature labour and the little one was born too soon, with lungs that were not fully developed. The foal survived for two days, but even with the best veterinary care was very weak and died peacefully, lying beside Lexi. We filmed the story on *Countryfile*; I was too broken to say much, but I put my farmer's hat on and said to the camera: 'It is heart-breaking, but we need to move on and hopefully have a foal next year.' I had to walk away to conceal my tears, but I was still accused of being heartless by a few viewers. Nothing could be further from the truth. Like everyone who works with animals, it's impossible not to be upset when one dies before its time. Not only had Lexi invested love and nurture into her baby, so had all of us involved in caring for her through her pregnancy. It was a very sad day for us all. But that's how it is in farming: we have good years, bad years, years when all our animals thrive, other years when we have more than our share of difficult births, and along with that comes death. Although to lose a foal for a rare breed horse was particularly sad, we had to hope for better news in the future.

I was relieved that I'd made the decision not to try to foal her myself though, because I would have felt very guilty, and blamed myself for it going wrong. Because Lexi was in the hands of real experts who had done everything possible for her foal, I knew there was nothing that could have been done to avoid it. Lexi initially seemed bemused when the foal was born: perhaps she wasn't ready, either. But after a couple of days she had started to bond with the little one. She was very quiet afterwards, not calling for her foal, but very subdued.

At least there was some good news on the horizon. Restrictions started to be lifted in July, and because we are an outdoor venue, we were among the first places able to welcome the public in again. We had to make lots of changes and put stiff protocols in place, which meant a lot of work for the team, and Kate in particular, but we were all buoyed by a sense of relief and anticipation.

Everyone who works here genuinely loves having the public around, and without them, for those staff who worked through lockdown looking after the animals and other essential work, there was a gloomy air to the place. Even the animals, I'm sure, missed their regular interaction with excited young faces. They have personalities, and some of the more extrovert ones thrive on the attention and adoration – especially Strawberry, our tame cow, who has been delighting families for years. She is so used to being handled and fussed over that she misses visitors when the park is closed, and during lockdown we had to spend extra time just being company for her. Before Covid struck we used to do milking demonstrations, when the public could watch Strawberry being milked. When the park was closed, we could no longer milk her for the public display, but she had masses of milk. So now we cross her with an Albion bull each year and when she has her calf, our livestock manager Mike Caunter buys in two or three calves from a nearby dairy herd, and she rears them as well as her own. We let them in to her in the morning and again at night, the same timetable as we would milk her, and she stands there placidly eating her breakfast or tea, the calves feeding away.

Cows usually only have one calf, but a small percentage give birth to twins, and when this happened in our Gloucester herd, Dad dubbed them 'Double Gloucesters', with a nod to the famous Double Gloucester cheese, to the delight of the local newspaper. The cow coped with them both very well, and we've had more twins in the same family line in our herd, a bit like twins running in families in human beings, I guess. There is a strong risk if the twins are male and female that the female will be infertile, having picked up male characteristics while she shared a uterus with her twin brother. She is called a freemartin, the name probably meaning that she is 'free' to be fattened with the males, in time to be slaughtered for Martinmas in November. There are other explanations of the name, but this is the one I like best.

It wasn't just Strawberry who missed the attention of our visitors. A few greedy goats cast a forlorn eye at me when I wandered, on my own, around their fields – they're used to being hand-fed by visitors. And the Gloucestershire Old Spots and the Exmoor ponies looked at me in disappointment. Where are our friends? Where are our admirers? Although we all tried to give them as much of our time as we could, it was poor compensation. I like to think they were as delighted as we were when the public came back in July 2020

Before the Park reopened, Prince Charles, now King Charles, paid us a visit. We had a phone call from the Lord Lieutenant of Gloucestershire, Edward Gillespie, telling us he would like to come. The King has always been a supporter of farms and farmers, and he is a fan of open farms which encourage the public to see where their food comes from. He was also very keen to see the countryside open up again after the pandemic.

It was a great accolade that he was coming to us, but Duncan and I were both a little nervous, and keen to make sure the visit ran smoothly and to time, so we walked through the tour a couple of times, rehearsing it.

It was a drizzly day when we showed him round, but he wasn't fazed by the weather and it was clear that he knows a great deal about the preservation of rare breeds. Of course, the Farm Park residents made him feel welcome: the goats came across at a gallop when I rattled a bucket of feed, and when he met a Gloucester Old Spot sow he was almost run over by her piglets, who led a charge to the feed trough.

To my surprise, His Majesty, like his late mother, asked after Archie. He knew we had had a Balmoral bull. I explained that Archie was now living six miles up the road on another farm, with another happy harem. Instead the King met Archie's successor, a black Highland bull called Black Prince, who I'd bought from a breeder in Worcestershire.

He won the Yearling Highland Bull class at the Royal Three Counties Show a year before we got him, but he was still a young bull. I had a choice between him and his father, who was a fantastic-looking mature bull, but was obviously very lively. He was in a field, roaring and pawing the ground, and I instinctively knew that he would be hard for me to handle, especially as I need animals to be calm to live at the Farm Park, given all the onlookers.

Black Prince on the other hand allowed me to walk up to him in his field and give him a friendly scratch behind his ears. He was already halter trained. I remember what Dad said about choosing a docile, friendly animal: always remember that his calves will carry half of their genes from him, and what you want in a cow is a good maternal instinct and a placid temperament. You give yourself a good start if you choose a quiet bull. Black Prince ticked that box, and he is a good-looking fella, too.

Prince will have to move on in a couple of years, because his first calves were born in 2021 and the females are with our herd. It will be a sad day because he's a firm favourite, but I know he'll find a new home easily enough, as he's proved his worth as a bull, and some other lucky cows will welcome him, I'm sure.

After our royal visit, the Farm Park finally reopened on 4 July. It was a soft launch because of course we could not open everywhere: the animal handling and the animal demonstrations were closed, and the soft play area was off limits. Hand sanitiser dispensers had to be installed all over the site, masks had to be worn in the barns and the shop, food and drink was all outside, numbers admitted were restricted and all bookings had to be done online. Like everywhere else, we became a cashless site.

None of this mattered when the first family came

through the gates into the park. I was there to see the first arrivals and, just as I'd shed a tear when we announced the closure, now I welled up with happiness. It was such an emotional moment, and I could see on the faces of the rest of the staff that they felt the same.

Covid had not done with us though; the next months were a constant juggling act with staff off having caught the virus, or having bereavements in their families. It was the same across the country and I'm not complaining because we managed everything, and the alternative, staying closed, would have been unbearable.

Nothing could rival the joy of reopening. Air travel was still off and many hospitality sites were still closed, so people flocked back to us. They, too, had had a miserable time cooped up, especially with small children, struggling with home schooling and just the sheer boredom of children not being allowed to run free with their friends, so now they were thrilled to come out for a day in the fresh air combined with all the animal experiences of the Farm Park. Our camp sites and the lodges were fully booked – not just for that year, but for the next too, with quite a few re-bookings for people who had lost out during lockdown. If they could not go abroad, it seemed families were determined to have some time enjoying themselves.

And then came Christmas; by far the most special Christmas the Farm Park has ever had. We felt it was important that the Christmas theme should reflect the dislocation we had all felt, and the vital need to re-establish a sense of togetherness, even in the strange world of masks, hand sanitising and keeping our distance from each other. We wanted a theme which emphasised coming together, being part of a bigger whole than just our own close families. For children in particular, we wanted the experience to be about friendship and sharing, and the joy of meeting up with others again, after the enforced separations we had all endured.

The theme we chose was the Enchanted Gathering, and the journey started with the Hare welcoming everyone on their quest to find the Wise Reindeer, who was keeping and protecting the Spirit of Christmas for us all. Along the trail other animals joined in, until everyone met together at the Gathering, symbolising, we hoped, how much we all need each other and a sense of togetherness. The story was told in rhymes along the route, and there was one particularly moving point for me.

As the twinkling lights led past the metal statue of a bull, erected at the Farm Park in memory of my dad, the poem read:

> *This magnificent beast is called Inspiration,*
> *Made in loving memory of farmer Joe Henson.*
> *In a year like no other, finding inspiration has*
>   *been tough,*
> *There have been moments when we all*
>   *sighed 'Enough'.*
> *As we approach the end of this strange year*
> *Look to the stars and be proud you made it here.*

Together we did it, we made it through
The world is wonderful because of
            people like you.
So if you ever feel it's too hard to go on
Remember to look up, to feel inspiration.

My dad has always been my inspiration, and it was special to feel that he was now providing inspiration for the visitors to the park who had, like all of us, been through a very difficult and often lonely year. The large metal sculpture of a White Park bull was based on a bull Dad once had, a big chap who was called Inspiration, so it was a fitting choice for a memorial to him, and now, after Covid, a name that was perfect for our theme of bringing everyone back together.

One December evening, I went up to the Farm Park to see how it was all going. The delight on the faces of the children (and the adults) as they discovered the special magic of Christmas was very moving. With my own children now grown up, that extra-special wonderment – when belief in Father Christmas still holds – is over, and seeing those little wide-eyed faces captivated by the age-old magic of it makes all the hard work and planning worthwhile. Also, however familiar with the park I am, seeing it lit up like this gives even me a new perspective on it. It made me think about Dad – and Mum, who we lost in 2019 – and how much they would both have enjoyed the way the Farm Park has developed, and especially the Christmas magic that it now holds.

172

Our visitors weren't just enchanted by the light trail. Our animals featured too. Almost like a Christmas miracle for us, Lexi was pregnant again. We had sent her to run with a stallion at Holbeache Farm, not too far away in Worcestershire, which is run by Suffolk experts and superfans, Mike and Alison Clarke. By the end of 2020 she had gained weight steadily and healthily, a scan showed she was pregnant, and we were nervously looking forward to what spring 2021 would bring.

We always aim to have some young animals to show visitors at Christmas: piglets, baby goats, and one of our five donkeys will have a foal, which is always a star attraction. Although lambing time for our sheep starts in February and runs through to the end of April, we have a small flock of twenty-five Poll Dorset sheep who deliver their lambs in autumn, so there are always some cute little ones on show. They are an unusual breed because they come into season in April and give birth towards the end of the year. If the winter weather is mild enough these lovely little lambs are strong enough to go out into the fields. It's a bit special seeing lambs in the fields at Christmas, but they have a really good fleece and can withstand the weather.

Father Christmas is a regular feature, and around him we gather the animals of the traditional Christmas nativity scene: cattle in the shape of Strawberry, lambs, a donkey. We throw in some baby goats to make up for the fact we don't have camels.

We actually used to have reindeer, when I was a child,

but Dad had a nasty experience with Rudolph, the bull reindeer. He was normally a placid fellow who towed us kids around on a sledge in the snow, or on a grass sledge when there was no snow. But Dad unfortunately came between Rudolph and his harem during the rutting season, when the big fella was getting frisky with his cows. He clearly thought Dad was a rival for their affections and attacked him so badly he nearly killed him. He had Dad pinned to the ground by his antlers, which Dad was holding on to. The large, strong animal began shaking his head, and luckily Dad's screaming brought the stockman running, who had to beat Rudolph off with a large stick. It was quite a struggle to release Dad, and the attack could easily have been fatal. After that, Dad decided it wasn't safe to keep the herd. Besides, he wanted to concentrate on native British breeds. Rudolph and his girls flew off to Whipsnade Zoo.

By the end of 2020, what had looked like being the worst year in the fifty-year history of the Farm Park turned out rather well. With restricted numbers we were still down on what we had originally planned for the year, but such a massive improvement on how the world had looked when lockdown was announced. It was a Christmas to remember.

11

Charlie's Story

I started this book by saying that increasingly I'd been reflecting on the importance of Christmas; that it's about being together, and is a time for family. This was truly brought home to me in Christmas 2021. It was the best Christmas of my life, because it was the Christmas that Charlie and I feared could be her last, and thankfully she survived to see it.

2021 started as the worst year of my life. Charlie was diagnosed with pancreatic cancer, one of the most feared cancers of all. With symptoms so difficult to spot, the disease has usually taken hold by the time treatment starts, with a survival rate of only around 5 per cent.

The whole experience has been brutal, and the treatment difficult. Watching her suffer was heart-breaking. For weeks we lived on a knife-edge, unsure whether her disease was terminal. We were told she had pancreatic cancer, but there was a possibility it was a rarer type which is less invasive and has a better prognosis. It was a terrible time for me; Charlie is my soulmate, we have two wonderful children together and I cannot imagine life without her. But it was of course many, many times worse for her. As it is her story, not mine, I think you should hear it in her words. For the rest of this chapter, wherever you see sans serif text, that's Charlie speaking.

Firstly I'd like to say that I'm a very private person and talking about my experience is not something I'm very comfortable with. Pancreatic cancer is often diagnosed too late and I I hope my story can highlight the desperate need for a screening system for early detection. Pancreatic Cancer UK is an amazing charity trying to promote this; if anyone needs help or advice please contact them.

Looking back, I had some symptoms for at least twelve to eighteen months before I was diagnosed. At first it did not seem like anything to worry about, just a windy, burbling stomach, occasionally needing a quick dash to the loo. It didn't flag up as anything serious, but it persisted. I wondered if I was developing an intolerance to certain foods. My mum has a low tolerance of dairy, so I tried cutting back, especially on cheese. It made no difference, although I did have spells when the symptoms seemed to go away for a few days. I realise now that I was looking for answers and I didn't really know what the questions were.

Charlie had a bad tummy over Christmas 2020 and we talked about it a few times, but she is very good at just getting on with things, and so I wasn't overly worried at that stage. After our daughter Ella was born she had colic, and Charlie was advised to try cutting out broccoli, cauliflower and cheese, so we had those conversations again. But by February 2021 things were bad enough for her to make a non-urgent appointment with our GP.

When they said there would be a three week wait to see the GP I didn't worry; I genuinely thought it might have cleared up by then.

But it hadn't, and she was asked by the doctor to supply stool samples. We were both wondering if she could have picked up a farm bug, although we weren't aware of any on the farm. Sometimes, if an animal is symptomless, it can pass an infection onto a human without being suspected as the culprit. For Charlie, it was March before she really started to worry.

I'd gone to a friend's house for lunch to watch Cheltenham Races on television and it was the first time I confided in others. Only Adam and my close family knew I was unwell at this point, but I'd had a really bad morning and couldn't cover up how bad I was feeling. By now I had regular diarrhoea, I was washed out and drained. I felt it had gone on too long, but the tests the GP had run were not showing anything up. I hadn't lost a huge amount of weight at

177

this stage, I put this down to the fact that I like food and still had a good appetite, even though my tummy was upset.

We were on holiday in Cornwall when the GP rang to say all the previous tests, including a colonoscopy, had come back negative and the next step would be an absorption test. This is when a stool sample is tested to see how much food is being digested and how much is passing straight through the body. I had no idea that a lack of enzymes produced by the pancreas could cause this, but they are vital to break down sugar, fats and starches and without them the body is starved of the nutrients that we get from food.

Signs of pancreatic cancer are ambiguous: back pain, indigestion, weight loss, loss of appetite, all of which can have other causes. A lesser known one is a change in bowel habits caused by the lack of enzymes. Things to look out for are soft poo that often floats, a greasy layer on the toilet water, sometimes even small globules of oil, and a distinctive, horrible smell (the correct medical term is steatorrhoea). Not that everyone gets this, which is why pancreatic cancer is so hard to diagnose. There are many different symptoms, and almost all of them can be put down to other conditions.

My symptoms were erratic; sometimes my stomach was really upset and I felt washed out, other times I didn't. I had lost maybe 10lbs by now and this was definitely unusual. After several days the GP rang to say that the malabsorption tests showed I wasn't absorbing food properly and this was most likely due to an inefficient pancreas. She prescribed a drug called Creon, which provides artificial enzymes, and is taken with food to replace the natural enzymes. It is made from the pancreas of a pig, which for me as a vegetarian is hard to process, but not taking them wasn't an option.

By this point I had done what we are all told not to do: googled my symptoms, which bought up pancreatic cancer, so I asked if this was a possibility. She assured me that this was highly unlikely but agreed it would be sensible to organise a scan to be safe. She said the dietitian would need to see me and might ask for a scan so it would save them having to do one. I started taking the Creon which immediately helped stabilise me and, on the whole, I relaxed thinking we had pretty much resolved the problem.

I went on my own for the scan at Cheltenham General Hospital. Adam offered to come, but there were still Covid restrictions in place, so he wouldn't have been allowed in with me. While I was waiting to go in for the scan I was overcome by a terrible foreboding, a feeling of utter fear and dread. I'd never felt anything like it before and I was absolutely convinced there was something seriously wrong. I didn't tell my family this had happened and tried to ignore it, telling myself I was just nervous because of the scan, but I think from that moment, deep down, I knew I was in trouble.

Once Charlie was settled on Creon her symptoms stabilised and we got on with normal life. She seemed fit and well, was working, walking miles with the dogs most days and we were enjoying a good social life.

The scan results took more than five weeks and the length of wait lulled us into a false sense of security. After all, most of us would assume no news is good news. Looking back we should have chased them up earlier but it's so easy to find reasons to carry on as normal and not face reality, and this was a classic case of burying our heads in the sand – which of course solves nothing.

At the beginning of August, I was working in Scotland and Charlie was at home on her own when the GP rang with the results from the scan.

There was no preamble, I was told the scan showed a four and a half centimetre growth on my pancreas, located in a difficult position and it was very serious. The GP told me I would be referred to a consultant ASAP. She asked if I had anyone with me at home and apologised that she had to discuss this over the phone, but said there was never an easy way to deliver this kind of news.

I felt I had been hit with a sledgehammer. I knew

enough about pancreatic cancer to know it had a very low survival rate. We knew of a couple of people who had had it, and their disease had progressed very quickly from diagnosis. I decided not to ring Adam; he was working and what could he do? I rang my amazing mum, who lives five minutes away, and she and Pete, her partner of many years, came straight over and stayed with me. I honestly don't know what I would have done without them, they were incredible – but I was in absolute hell, I couldn't process it, it was too big to take in. The day passed in a blur of phone calls booking me in for more tests and appointments. Eventually Adam rang from the airport as he was waiting to fly home, and I told him.

For me, it was a huge shock. By nature I'm a pragmatist, which probably comes from being a farmer. I deal in facts, I work out what can be done, but in this situation I was totally lost. I tried to go into 'Right this is the problem, we will deal with it day to day and I will find a solution' mode, but I was terrified. I knew I needed to be strong and support Charlie and the kids but how do you do that? Our lives would never be the same and I had to try to find a way to get us through this nightmare. It was a very long flight home.

Within a few days we were at Gloucestershire Royal Hospital, sitting in a small room with a registrar and a nurse. Yes, we were told, it is cancer, but there is a possibility it could be a rare, slow-growing type of pancreatic cancer, a neuro-endocrine tumour, which in some (but not all) cases may be treatable. Only 2 per cent of pancreatic cancer is neuro-endocrine, but because Charlie had had symptoms for a long time, she was relatively well, and there was no sign it had spread, they suspected it could be this type. However, we were warned that even if this was the case, treatment would be tricky because of the size and position of the tumour and they could only make further decisions once they had all the facts.

Charlie was told that to make an accurate diagnosis she would need to do a urine test which involved collecting every drop of her pee for twenty-four hours. It would then be sent off to a lab and take twenty-eight days for them to work out what we were dealing with. The results would need to be discussed with a multidisciplinary team once they were through. As he was leaving the room the registrar dropped the bomb: if it was not neuro-endocrine, there was a distinct possibility all they could do was offer palliative care.

We were both stunned. It is hard to blame medical professionals who deal with life or death every day, but when they deliver a statement like that, so matter-of-factly, the effect is devastating. We were left with so many more questions than answers but at this stage it seemed there wasn't a great deal more they could tell us, so we just had to wait.

Charlie was issued with a very large pot with a lid for her pee collection, then we were sent to another department to do blood tests.

I could hardly walk, my legs felt they would give way and Adam had to almost carry me down the corridor. The prospect of waiting twenty-eight days for a result was horrifying; with potentially so little time left I could hardly bear the thought of spending it in limbo. As we walked down the corridors other patients naturally recognised Adam, and stared at us. When we got to the blood test department I was lying on a bed sobbing and I could hear Adam talking to some of the staff who had also recognised him. He wasn't allowed in with me, but I knew he was trying to be kind when he must have been so broken.

We were both very quiet when we got into the car to drive home, trying to process the enormity of what had happened to us. It was on that drive that Charlie asked me something very important.

I told Adam I wanted to get married. We had been together for many years and had never felt we needed to marry; for me, having children with Adam was our commitment to each other. We have always been very independent people, I'm not one for convention and neither of us relished the thought of a big traditional wedding, which can be stressful and very expensive. Over the years we'd once or twice chatted about doing a Drive-thru Elvis wedding in Las Vegas, but it had never been important.

Now, suddenly, it was the *most* important thing in the world. It's ridiculous, and I don't know why, but I really, really wanted everyone to know how much I love Adam; most importantly, I wanted him to know. I wanted our children to know how bonded we are. It had never mattered before, but it was suddenly such a big thing that I was married to him.

When Charlie said it, I was still struggling to process the news we'd heard at the hospital, and my first reaction was that I would love to marry Charlie but how would we manage to organise a wedding on top of everything ... My practical mind was dealing with the fallout of the medical news, I really didn't know how to even start on a wedding ...

On our way home we called in to see Sue, Charlie's mum, and after filling her in on the news from the appointment, told her we were going to get married. She and Charlie's sisters, Vicky and Katharin, got busy organising. Katharin managed to get us the first date possible at Stroud Register Office, 9 September, and we worked around that. They were all incredible and took so much of the stress out of the planning, as well as supporting Charlie as she struggled to come to terms with her situation. Practically the only thing that we had to do was go for an interview in Gloucester, producing the documents we needed to prove we were legally free to marry.

Looking back, the wedding was a great distraction,

giving us both something positive to concentrate on.

For me, the full impact of what was happening hit me at our regular Thursday morning meeting with Duncan and the senior management team at the Farm Park. I had to tell them I would need time off work in the coming weeks and the reason why. I tried to say the words and completely broke down. I had been trying so hard not to do it in front of Charlie, but saying it out loud really brought the enormity of the situation home.

We were all doing our best to keep things upbeat for Charlie. Her friends were unbelievable, organising walks, lunches and other distractions. Ella and Alfie were in the picture from the start: we have always been open with them, although we weren't brutally honest.

There was no point in telling them everything would be fine when we knew, whatever the results of the tests, I had a huge battle ahead of me. It's impossible to keep a brave face on all the time and they deserved to know how serious it was so we could make the most of whatever time we had left. They were both amazing, I'm so proud of the way they coped and supported me when it must have been so incredibly difficult for them.

I got together with Charlie's sisters and her mum to stress the need to be positive. For Charlie, it was a very difficult time.

CHRISTMAS ON THE FARM

All I could do was clean the house and walk the dogs. Anyone who knows me will know I've never been an avid cleaner, but it felt like something I could control, while I had no control over anything else. I couldn't concentrate long enough to read or watch television.

Although it felt like being in limbo, practical things were happening. The idea of a twenty-eight-day wait for the results of the urine test was unbearable. Before we were together properly, Charlie and her sister Vicky shared a flat in London with Vicky's then boyfriend JJ, who was a medical student. They bought a flat together, the three of them, and JJ had gone on to have a very successful career in medicine. Even though he and Vicky had split up and both married other people, he kept in touch. Vicky messaged him and asked for advice on who we should consult for a second opinion on Charlie's scan.

JJ came back to us within minutes and recommended Professor Giuseppe Fusai, who has a string of great qualifications and is one of Britain's leading experts in pancreatic surgery. Vicky sent me the info and I made the phone calls from the farm office, because I did not want to do it in front of Charlie. I was immediately reassured by Professor Fusai's secretary that he could help, and then I had to arrange for her scan to be sent to him electronically. He received it on a Friday, told us he would look at it over the weekend, and be in touch on Monday.

Duncan was, as ever, incredibly supportive and the

first to offer financial help from the business if we needed it.

On Monday Professor Fusai rang me. Charlie, her mum and sisters had gone out for a walk, so I was able to talk openly to him. It was good news: there was no sign the cancer had spread and he felt it was operable. He still did not know if it was neuro-endocrine, and he stressed that it would be a very tricky operation, but he felt he could do it.

It was like someone gave me back a tiny bit of hope. It felt like winning the Lottery 5,000 times.

More investigation was needed, and everything began to happen fast. Three days after his call we were in London for Charlie to have a biopsy, followed the next day by a PET scan combined with an MRI. Charlie is claustrophobic and was sedated and given a blindfold before the MRI so that she was unaware of the machinery.

The results came quickly: the scan was on a Friday and by Tuesday we heard the outcome. It was a Stage One cancer, it was neuro-endocrine and although it was in a difficult place, Professor Fusai had consulted his colleagues and he was confident he could operate. He was cautious, but optimistic. The main worry was that Charlie's tumour had grown around the portal vein, the main vein that drains blood from the pancreas, gall bladder, spleen and gastro-intestinal tract into the liver. Only a small channel in this vein was working, because the vein was partially blocked by the tumour. He would have to take the vein out and insert a donor vein, which would function for long enough to allow the blood to establish other routes, through smaller veins, to the liver. To attach a donor vein he would need a bit of Charlie's vein to be left to graft onto, and he wasn't sure there would be enough.

We decided to go ahead – and actually put the date of the operation back by a week because of our wedding. Professor Fusai said that one week would make little difference, so we went ahead with our big day, and I am so, so glad we did, because it was the most wonderful day ever.

Charlie didn't go full bridal, but wore an ivory dress and looked beautiful. We couldn't have all our friends there, having organised the wedding at such short notice, but we promised them we would celebrate at a later date. We took bottles of fizz and friendship candles to many of them, so that they could drink a toast at the time we were tying the knot.

Charlie has two sisters and I have three, so with their husbands and our many nieces and nephews (only one couldn't come because he was in Australia), plus Charlie's mum and Pete, we had a small crowd. Two of Charlie's best friends, Suzanne and Sarah, came, with Sarah flying in from America, and my great mate Jam, who had lived with me back in my bungalow days, was also there.

Everyone knew that Charlie was going into hospital the next day and it was very emotional. When I saw her walking in on the arm of her mum, I had to struggle to hold it together. Alfie was my best man, Ella was chief bridesmaid and there were lots of tears, and a great deal of love. The registrar knew nothing of what was happening in our lives, but she commented that it was one of the most loving and emotional weddings she had ever presided over.

There were also funny moments that lightened the mood. Ella and Alfie, knowing that I am a great fan of vintage Ford Mustang cars, had hired one as a surprise to take us from the registry office to the reception, which was at No. 131, a venue in Cheltenham. The car wouldn't start and Jam, who owns a local garage, took his jacket off and got under the bonnet, laughing: 'Now I know why you invited me.'

The reception was amazing. The food was wonderful, there was a musician playing and the cousins had a great time; they rarely all get together, and this was the first time they were all old enough to enjoy a drink – it was so lovely to see, especially as they made the most of the cocktails.

A friend of Charlie's sister, Katharin, is a professional photographer, and took the pictures in exchange for a donation to charity which was such a lovely gesture. Charlie couldn't drink, of course, so I was also very restrained. We both made very emotional speeches, along with Jam and the children; lots of tears were shed.

Later that afternoon we sat around on the veranda catching up with everyone and then spent a quiet evening over dinner before we retired to our bedrooms. The cousins, now joined by some of Alfie's and Ella's friends, hit the town and staggered back at some ridiculous hour. All in all, it was a lovely day, and we tried very hard not to think of what was hanging over us.

The next day, back home, Charlie had to prepare to go into hospital, and it felt as if the world was on pause. Suzanne and Sarah joined us for lunch, which lightened the atmosphere, but then Charlie, Ella, Alfie and I set off for London, where she was booked into hospital for 6 p.m. Because of Covid restrictions, we had to drop her outside; we weren't even allowed into the foyer with her. It was an emotional goodbye. I'll never forget the feeling of complete helplessness watching her walk through the doors.

The children and I really needed to be close by even though there was nothing we could do, and fortunately some lovely friends offered to let us stay at their house. Ella, Alfie and I made our way there. I'm not sure how we got through the next twenty-four hours, it was impossible to sleep or think about anything other than Charlie. Everything started at 7 a.m. the next day, it was the longest of days, and we spent it wandering around London. Two of Ella's friends joined us; they all enjoy shopping in charity shops so I have vague memories of going into a few, and we must have stopped somewhere for lunch, but the whole day is a blur. We knew the operation would be long, and I had also been told that if anything went wrong I would be summoned to the hospital immediately. As the afternoon ticked by we were desperate for news, but beginning to feel hopeful that she must be nearly through it.

We were on the South Bank, discussing how to get back to our accommodation (Alfie reminded me that we could not go on the tube because we might not have a phone signal) when, at 4.30 p.m., my phone finally rang. It was Professor Fusai and he didn't mess around, telling me straightaway that the operation went well, he was very pleased, and that Charlie was stable in recovery, in intensive care.

The kids were looking at me anxiously as we spoke so I grinned and put my thumbs up to let them know the news was good. After the call we had a very emotional group hug, the relief was indescribable. As she was so poorly we were not allowed to see her, but it felt like an enormous weight had been lifted and we were able to quietly relax that evening. I had lots of phone calls to make, to update all our family and friends.

For the three days that she was in intensive care, no one was allowed to visit. Once she was moved to her room we were told only one of us could go in each day, and only for an hour. In fact, the hospital did not stick to the one-hour rule: I was usually there for three to four hours. Charlie's mum and Ella also visited her. Alfie, at Charlie's insistence, had gone back to uni.

Charlie was in hospital ten days in all. It's a massive

operation, known as the Whipple Procedure, which involves removing the wide part of the pancreas and some other organs, like the gallbladder and part of the duodenum. It was a shock when I first saw her because she had drains and drips and tubes coming out from all over her, and she looked very poorly. The most uncomfortable tube went through her nose and down her throat, draining bile from her stomach; this stayed in for three days, despite her begging them to remove it. There was a central catheter into her neck, with more than one line, which was also very uncomfortable. Her legs were swollen to twice their normal size. The medical attention was first class.

I felt in really safe hands. Professor Fusai was brilliant and checked on me regularly. The nursing staff were great – especially Angela, my cancer nurse, who was brilliant both in hospital and on the end of the phone once I got home, for reassurance and advice.

I remember the anaesthetist who came to see me on the evening before the operation saying that the most important thing I could do was to start moving as soon as I could, even if it was only a little. He said that moving around would help me get better, and that became my mantra. In hospital, with all the drips and drains attached, I started to walk across the room for couple of minutes, then progressed to walking along the corridor, trying to do a bit more each day. I felt physically broken, but I knew I had to help myself get better. It gave me purpose and allowed me to focus my mind on the future for the first time in months.

As soon as I could walk up and down stairs I was allowed home, still with one drain in which was taking lymph fluid from the pancreas into a bag. I had to be shown how to empty this and record the amount of fluid to ensure I was progressing.

As soon as Charlie walked into the farmhouse, the dogs went mad. I was terrified that Olive, the Hungarian Viszla, would jump up and knock the drain out, they were so excited to see her, and she was so frail after such an enormous operation. Rules were broken, and Minnie, the dachshund, was allowed upstairs to lie on her bed – there was no chance of that not happening! The animals are so important to her, they brought so much solace and pleasure to her, I'm absolutely convinced they helped with her physical and mental recovery.

We started taking walks up and down the farm drive, and I am full of admiration for her because it is so easy just to lie in bed when you feel rubbish. Within two weeks of coming home, Charlie could walk half a mile.

For me it was control again. If I could make myself walk, I was still alive. I remember going out one day when it was raining heavily, and it was like the most life-affirming thing I have ever done. I didn't care about getting soaking wet, I was alive! You have no idea how the stupidest things can be so important. It felt like a joy and a privilege to be walking in the rain, when before I would probably have moaned it was too wet to leave the house.

Two or three months after the op we were invited to a birthday party, with a 1920s theme. I was waiting for Charlie downstairs, and she walked into the kitchen dressed up ready to go. She looked so beautiful. It really hit me how close I had been to losing her.

Recovery is ongoing, and we live from one six-monthly scan to the next. At every meal Charlie has to take a handful of Creon capsules, she has to take blood thinners because the blood is now routed through smaller veins, and she has to take iron supplements. Her iron was so low after the op that she needed an infusion.

Remembering to take enough Creon was difficult at first, and I slipped up a few times, with a gripey tummy afterwards to remind me to do better in future. My pancreas no longer produces any enzymes naturally so I have to rely completely on artificial ones. If I eat a small snack like an apple, I take two capsules. For a normal breakfast, around six, and for a roast dinner, six to eight. For a three-course meal out – well, the good thing is you can't overdose on them! At first I was constantly thinking 'Did I take my tablets?' I am better now, but it's a lifetime commitment. Fortunately I have not become diabetic which can happen after this surgery, so my insulin levels are checked regularly.

Having a scan is absolutely terrifying. The worry starts to build up a couple of months beforehand, then there is the wait for the result, which is all consuming. If you get a clear scan, and thank God, I have so far had clear results, it is the best gift in the world. You have six months of your life back that you thought you might not have.

We have made a point of doing lots of things together since Charlie came back home. Travel is something we both love and we've tried to fit in as much as possible. Ella and her boyfriend Sam finally managed to go off on their travels in 2022, following my post-college itinerary in the loosest of ways, as it included New Zealand and Australia. But they also decided they wanted to go to Japan, and in March 2023, we went to meet them. It meant so much to see them, though it was hard to wave them off at the end of the trip; Japan was a fantastic place.

Everything in life is different after the experience we've both been through. Our family and friends are even more important to us; we are so lucky to have them and are forever grateful for their support. I sometimes get annoyed with Charlie for worrying about small things, but she's quick to point out that life has to go on and we can't be always be defined by what she's been through. Our experience means we both want to make the absolute most of life, say yes to things and make time for what's important. It's such a cliché, but nothing is as important as your health.

In May 2023 Charlie went back to work, two days a week. When we first got together she had a career in television as a production manager, and now she is working as location manager on a BBC series. It's incredible to watch her get back to normal life; something which, at one point, we didn't think would ever happen.

Christmas 2021 was very special. Charlie was getting better and stronger all the time. We planned to spend the break in Cirencester with Charlie's sister Vicky, her husband Justin and their three children, Elliott, Willow and Cecily. It would mean that Alfie, who is a student at Exeter University, would have company of his own age with his three cousins. Ella was travelling by then – we encouraged her to go and make the most of life, and felt that was even more important after what we'd been through. The gathering was set to include Charlie's mum Sue, and Justin's parents, Alan and Jane.

But, as we all know, the best laid plans ... On the morning of Christmas Day itself, Elliott tested positive for Covid, and the whole family had to isolate. Charlie's mum was actually on the doorstep of Vicky's house carrying some of the veg when she got the news, relayed from behind the closed door. Everyone was quickly diverted to Bemborough farmhouse, where we had not been expecting to host Christmas or cook lunch, but everyone pitched in. After all Charlie had been through I don't think cooking was on her agenda, but we worked together and created a feast. Charlie's mum brought her vegetables, we raided the freezer and one way and another we had plenty to eat.

It wasn't what we had planned, but we just got on with it and all had a good time. It reminded us to be positive, make the most of the situation and not to stress over the small things. I felt sorry for Alfie – he spent his Christmas with, by his standards, a rather elderly crew, but he mucked in and made the best of it.

As for us, it was a very special time. We came so close to never having another Christmas together, so a small change to our plans was not going to derail our day. The main thing was that Charlie was doing well, and we still had some, if not all, of our precious family around us. In many ways, it felt wonderful to end the year in our home, steeped in memories of so many happy Christmases, and we were now celebrating it for the first time as husband and wife.

12

Christmas Present and Christmas Future

Nowadays we sell Christmas trees at the Farm Park, so in 2022 I popped across to pick one up. I thought back to Dad lopping one down in the woods next to the farmhouse, and Mum's reaction every year. I tried not to get one that was too tall . . .

Charlie has much more refined taste than our 1970s tree, and she decorates it beautifully, in one colour, and definitely NO tinsel. One year, while she was out, Ella, Alfie and I draped multi-coloured tinsel all over it after we brought it in, just to wind her up.

It was such a cold December, with far too much snow. It was difficult for us to keep all the water troughs for the animals unfrozen, but while that was hard work for us, at least the children and adults who were walking our Christmas trail at night were especially excited to see the frost on the fields glistening in the lights.

One day when I had a couple of hours free time, and

as I was over there anyway, I decided to walk up to the gorse valley where the Exmoors spend the winters along with Lexi, the Suffolk Punch.

You'll remember that in December 2020, Lexi was expecting a foal. It was in the spring of our stressful 2021 that she went back to Holbeache and to the experts, Alison and Mike, to give birth. We were all nervous; Alison and Mike have masses of experience and I trust them implicitly, but it was still a worrying week or two, at a time when Charlie and I had other major worries to contend with. This time we were cautious about publicising the birth, because we were all concerned that the previous year's experience could be repeated. Perhaps Lexi would always struggle to take a foal to full term, perhaps we were in for another heartbreak.

I'm pleased to say that, like the great girl she is, Lexi foaled at full term in mid-May, a colt. We called him Braveheart, a name chosen by Charlie, because he would grow into a big animal with a big heart, and because I had appeared in the film *Braveheart*.

Two weeks later he and his mum came back to the farm. He was immediately a great success with the staff and the visitors, and Lexi proved to be a wonderful mother. Seeing Braveheart wobble after Lexi was an uplifting moment in a year that would get much worse before it got better.

We were all very happy Lexi had delivered a healthy colt, but we couldn't help but want a filly for her, given how important they are to the survival of the breed. So when Lexi was ready, we took her back to Holbeache to run with the stallion. Alison explained to me how important it is to breed the right mare with the right stallion, for genetic reasons. The numbers of the breed are so low that there is always a danger of in-breeding, with animals that are too closely related. This causes deformities, problems giving birth, illnesses and weak offspring, so now breeders like Alison and Mike use a clever system called SPARKS, which stands for Single Population Analysis and Record Keeping System. Quite a mouthful, but it's a computer-based analysis of the genetic backgrounds of all Suffolk Punch horses. The system was devised to protect an even more at-risk horse, the Cleveland Bay, and to promote a healthy gene pool. It can also be used for animals in captivity in zoos. It's like the stud books that breeders keep, and the hand-written ledgers that traditional farmers had for the rams or bulls that would service their sheep or cows.

Alison can feed Lexi's details into the system and it will assess how good a match a stallion is for her. There is a traffic light system: green is a really good choice, red is a definite no, and yellow is okay. The system is endorsed by the Rare Breeds Survival Trust, and is helping to pull breeds that are close to disappearing forever back from the brink.

Soon after, Lexi was in foal again – great news. But when the vet came at in the winter of 2021 to scan her, he could not be sure, but thought it was more likely that it was another colt. Not bad news – a healthy birth was all we really wanted, but we couldn't help feeling a little disappointed. Once again, Lexi went back to Holbeache to give birth, and we all waited with our fingers crossed for her.

It was May Day 2022, a bank holiday, when the Farm Park was full of visitors, that the wonderful news came through. When I saw Alison's name come up on the screen of my phone, I answered the call immediately, and let out a whoop of joy when she told me that not only had Lexi had a successful birth, but the newborn was a filly. I dubbed Alison the miracle worker, because she could turn colts into fillies!

Lexi apparently decided to foal against a wall, which didn't make life easy for Alison who was on hand to help out, but everything went smoothly. 'She's very foal-proud, protective of the new arrival,' Alison told me.

We launched an appeal on social media and at the Farm Park for a name for our latest addition, and the result was Mayflower, a name that summed up that she was born on May Day, and is as pretty as a flower.

She came back to the farm four weeks later. Her spindly legs did not look strong enough to hold her body, she tossed her head shyly and nuzzled up to the comforting flank of her mother. Mayflower was definitely the most beautiful foal in the world – although I have to admit I am heavily biased. My eyes actually misted over when I first saw her uncertainly stepping down the ramp of the trailer that brought her home to our farm.

Alison helped me take her through to the field where the two of them would graze. Just in time, I remembered that our Exmoor stallion was in the next field, and I shut him away. The last thing we'd have wanted was him jumping over the wall, which has barbed wire on top, to get to Lexi. Not only would he have done himself harm, but if he went near her now she had her foal, she'd probably kick his chops in if he tried to get friendly with her. A close shave!

Mayflower wormed her way into my heart in the way that some animals do, especially as we had all been expecting Lexi to deliver another colt, a brother for Braveheart. To have a filly was a tremendous bonus. But that's not the only reason why I, and everyone else who sees her, falls in love with Mayflower. She really is a beautiful creature, as gentle and easy-going as her magnificent mother.

Hard to think of our pretty filly Mayflower ever being stout, but as she grows she is already acquiring the build of a Suffolk, and in time will be as big as her patient, loving mother Lexi. All Suffolks are a lovely colour, differing shades of chestnut. I'm told the proper old-fashioned spelling is chesnut, without the t.

Alison was as surprised as I was when she lifted the newborn's leg to find her a filly, but we of course don't blame the vet, because it is very hard to tell from the scan. Besides, Alison told me: 'What you get on the floor is what you get on the floor,' which is a good, philosophical attitude to take.

Alison's father Mike said: 'You can't put them back and ask for something different,' which I also rather like.

Alison explained that even if, like Braveheart, she had been a colt, it would still have been great news, just to have another Suffolk born. Colts can become stallions, for breeding, and they are also increasing in popularity for riding and, like the Shires, they are in growing demand for pulling carriages at shows and for special events.

Which brought me on to asking for an update on Braveheart. He is living with a Suffolk owner, Michael Yorke, where Alison has been keeping up with news of his training. He has been gelded, which means he won't be working as a stallion, but he will be trained to pull with a halter. He's already started training, on a long lead, and pulling a tyre around. By the time he is three, he will be introduced to a harness, and will eventually join Michael's team working at weddings, funerals and at ploughing competitions.

I'd heard that Braveheart kicked a bit when he was first handled, but Alison reassured me he had got over that. She also told me that, although Braveheart is still his official name, in training it is too much of a mouthful, so he's been renamed Wally. It's an appropriate name: William Wallace was the original Braveheart. I am looking forward to the day when I see this plucky little foal a fully grown, hard-working horse, helping everyone who sees him appreciate this magnificent breed.

The Exmoor stallion I didn't want jumping over the

wall to annoy Lexi was Willow Warbler. He's a sturdy little fellow, a great mate of mine. He's been loaned to us for breeding by Dai and Ruth Thomas, who run the Coedywern Stud in Bannau Brycheiniog (the Brecon Beacons), which is great terrain for Exmoor ponies. I like the fact that Dai and Ruth met when they were both studying at the Veterinary School at Edinburgh University, where they encountered the herd descended from the ponies originally given to the university by Mary Hetherington.

I could tell from first meeting Willow that he's a friendly chap, and he's also greedy, so a bit of food will always bring him running to greet me. He did his stuff with the ladies in the herd, who all seem to have taken to him, and rewarded us with foals in the spring. We always keep a couple of female foals for the herd, but otherwise we sell on the foals to others who want to preserve the breed.

I think horses remind me of Christmas because of Kitty and Sun Ray, the Shires who helped Dad get to all the animals when the snow fell fast and thick when I was just a child. They were so mesmerizingly good at their jobs. That's true of other heavy horse breeds too.

Shires were not the only ones Dad introduced to the farm. He was mates with Charlie Pinney, a famous heavy horse expert, who used to come to the Farm Park to run heavy horse training courses. Charlie, who sadly died far too young in 2007, dedicated his working life to these amazing animals, designing special chassis links to enable modern farm implements to be pulled by the original horse power. Charlie was evangelical about the use of horses instead of tractors: 'Living horse power is cheap and readily available,' he said. 'We can breed horses without limit, without endangering the planet. They can pull things, carry us, help support our society, feed it and enable it to function. They can do so far better than they did in the past if we take advantage of technical advances in machinery design. They don't destroy the environment, they enhance it,' he wrote in a very detailed paper for the Foundation for the Economics of Sustainability.

He spoke eloquently of the companionship of a heavy horse ploughing team – something you don't get from a tractor. Dad – and I – shared many of his sentiments. The sight of a heavy horse working, its coat glistening, its leather harness polished and trimmed with gleaming brass, is evocative and powerfully moving. But at the same time we both recognised the need to run Bemborough commercially, and we weren't getting rid of our tractors.

Still, Dad was keen to help preserve these magnificent old breeds, and he and Charlie set off on an adventure to France, to a horse sale. They bought five Ardennes, another breed of heavy horses native to the Ardennes region of France, Belgium and Luxembourg. Ardennes are very slightly smaller than Shires, with sturdy legs and very broad, muscular bodies. On the Continent they are used mainly for meat, and the horses they bought were all destined to be slaughtered for the table. Their tails had been docked to show off their large rumps, to attract the butchers. They were being held in sheds, like cattle. Those five had a very lucky break when Dad and Charlie turned up.

Back home, they were easy to train because they are docile, even-tempered animals. To reverse them you simply needed to put a hand on their chest and they would obediently move backwards into a harness. Dad bred from them for a number of years.

Heavy horses like Shires and Ardennes weren't showy horses to pull the gentry's carriages; they were more versatile, they lived long lives, and there were no temperamental moments. In short, the sort of workers any farmer wants, and watching them pull a plough, it's easy to see why they were known in days gone by as Kings of the Field.

I've had a go at ploughing behind a Shire at a famous ploughing competition, the Trumpet Agricultural Show, in Herefordshire. The competition has its roots back in the Second World War, when England was being urged to Dig for Victory, and the Home Guard was kept busy turning pasture into arable land. At the time, they used horses because it was impossible to get fuel for tractors. Meeting at the Trumpet Inn in Ledbury, they decided to start an annual show and ploughing competition, and today men and women from all over the country compete.

I'm in awe of the experts with their perfectly straight

furrows because, in the words I used to camera after my attempt, my furrow was 'as straight as a dog's hind legs'. You are supposed to achieve a furrow so straight that a mouse can be seen running the whole length along it, but my mouse would have slipped from view after a few yards. All ploughing, even with the advantage of the most modern machinery, is a skilled job, because you have to turn over the turf and bury all the weed and grass. I respect anyone who can do it well, and I like Benjamin Franklin's saying: 'A ploughman on his legs is higher than a gentleman on his knees.'

I'm happy to say that, although they will never compete with the massive farm machinery we deploy today, Shire horses are making a bit of a comeback, and there are areas of land management where they beat the internal combustion engine hands down. In woodland management, for example, they can step around saplings, avoid fallen logs, and in one day a man and a horse can singlehandedly shift ten tons of lumber, negotiating awkward areas where no mechanised vehicle could get. They are also being used for bracken rolling, which involves towing a roller across dense bracken to break stems and prevent it smothering other more diverse plant growth, and the Royal Parks are leading the way, using them wherever it makes sense. Added to this, they are growing in popularity for weddings and funerals, all of which means, I hope, a brighter future for this breed that is still on the endangered list.

And what about the future of farming in general, and

the way it's linked to our environment? Well, there is a great deal of talk in agriculture about 'regenerative farming', which means protecting and conserving the soil as well as the animals that live on it. It's the opposite of industrial farming, and it's something that we, at Bemborough, are naturally keen on. We are doing everything we can to make the farm and the Farm Park environmentally sustainable, but we are also aware that we have to be financially viable. It's no good following all the best environmental practices if at the end of the day the business loses money. Farmers are not very good at talking about money, and, as with some other professions, there's a perception that we are doing it because we love it (which we are) and therefore money doesn't come into it. It does. If the business is not on a sound footing it won't survive, however laudable its practices. If farms fail or farmers reduce the amount they produce because of their new regenerative ways, the country will end up importing more wheat and other crops, which will be counterproductive. This doesn't mean we shouldn't be looking at all the new ideas coming through about how to be more sustainable; we have already adopted quite a few, and I'm sure we will do more in future, but we need to do it carefully. It's a dilemma.

I had a wonderful opportunity to explore regenerative farming when I made three programmes about it for *Countryfile*, following different ways that farmers can improve their relationship with nature, and their soil in particular. Farming not far from me, just over the hill, is David Wilson, who was previously the farm manager at King Charles's Duchy Home Farm, where he helped pioneer sustainable organic agriculture. He now farms Fir Farm in a similar way, and because his land is the same as ours – Cotswold brash, which means it has a shallow depth, is lime rich and full of stones – it was easy to compare his with mine. He farms 800 acres, which is half the size of our farm. But whereas we use fertiliser, he does not use any, and he gives his sheep and cows no additives or supplements. He uses the dung from his cattle to fertilise his crops, and he grows a diverse range of plants, with different root structures, which break up the soil and improve its health. The legume, like clover and trefoil, fix nitrogen naturally into the soil.

It all sounds great, especially as the cost of fertiliser has risen exponentially. But would it work for us? David and I got together to compare notes over the course of the three programmes, one in spring at planting time, one in summer when the crops were high and then for the third time after we harvested them.

One of the first things we did was get a soil expert, Niels Corfield, to take samples of our soil – one each from our pasture, arable land and from the edges of the arable fields, to compare with a sample from David's land. He could immediately tell us that our margin soil contained more organic matter than our arable soil, and was, in fact, quite similar to David's. Our arable soil was more compacted, there was less microbial activity, the fungi and micro-fauna were not doing their work of breaking it up as well as on David's land. It astonished me to be told that one teaspoonful of good soil contains more microorganisms than there are people on the planet . . .

Once the samples were taken they were sent to a laboratory for testing. The results were better than I feared: my arable soil, which was the worst of my three samples, had a nice balance of bacteria, protozoa (single cell organisms), fungi and nematodes. However, David's soil had much more life in it, with thirty-one times as many types of amoeba than mine.

But would it be economic for us to change to David's system? In order to farm the way he does we would have to leave our land without crops for four years to improve the quality of the soil, and that's simply not economically possible. We grow 1,000 acres of high value crops, we get a higher yield than David, but he gets a better price for his heritage wheat than we do, and of course he has no chemical costs. The deal breaker is the four year wait for production to start. Also, if we produced less, even if it was high quality heritage wheat that sold at a premium, it would reduce the amount of wheat grown in this country, making us even more vulnerable to the import market. Fortunately, in the UK we import very little wheat from war-torn Ukraine, but we do rely on imports from Germany, Canada and the USA, and the aim must be for us to be self-sufficient. The more expensive wheat that is grown by David's methods is sold to make more expensive bread and other food products, at a time when consumers are struggling with food bills and looking for the cheapest deals.

David believes in growing old varieties of wheat to preserve the ancestors of the crops we grow today, in the same way that Dad wanted to preserve the DNA of the old breeds of British livestock, and I can see the sense of this.

The choice of how far to go into regenerative farming is a constant juggling act for us. We need to make our contribution to feeding the nation with our larger yield crops than David, but we can also see the advantages of his system for the land and ultimately the future of the planet. On balance, it would not make economic sense for us to switch completely to David's methods, and it would be disastrous for the country if all wheat farmers switched right now. Of course I can see that healthy soil produces healthy food, which in turn produces healthy people, but we realise that we cannot do it all in one go. It's a major conundrum, hugely complex, and we continue to ponder it.

But that doesn't mean we can't do some of the good practices that regenerative farming has pioneered. Our farm has 600 acres of pasture, on which we never grow arable crops. We use it for cutting grass to make sileage and grazing sheep. Could we make changes that would not impact on the profitability of the farm? We called in Jonty Brunyee from Farm-Ed, a not-for-profit organisation dedicated to helping farmers work in a more environmentally friendly way, who suggested we grow a richer variety of species on this land, with more clover and legumes to improve the soil. Clover seeds would cost us only two thirds of the price of fertiliser, with the huge bonus that we would only have to reseed every ten years, instead of fertilising every year.

We were already doing this with half of our pasture land, but we decided after talking to Jonty that we would not use any fertiliser on the remaining 300 acres and would plant clover, which fixes nitrogen into the soil (doing the same job as commercial fertilisers), and sainfoin, which is particularly suited to our soil, and has a very attractive pink flower.

We have also gone over to a method called 'min-till', which is shorthand for minimum tillage. This means rather than ploughing our arable fields, we plant our crops straight into the stubble, which reduces the amount of heavy machinery going across the land, easing the problem the soil experts identified of our soil being denser and compacted. It improves the soil health by keeping more of the valuable organisms in there, and it helps hold water in the soil, which will become increasingly important as climate change means we will all have to get used to drier weather.

It also means more carbon is held in the soil and not released into the atmosphere, and using the machinery less means a reduction in the greenhouse gases from the diesel (as well as a bonus for us in lower fuel costs). Carbon emission is something Duncan and I are very aware of, as we know that food production accounts for 10 per cent of the greenhouse gases that create the climate change problem, and we want to do as much as we can to cut our own contribution.

One of the many lessons I learned from Dad was always to consult someone who knows more than you do. As he said: 'you can't be an expert at everything'. That's why we decided to bring in a specialist company, Trinity Agtech, to measure our carbon footprint with a carbon calculator and since we got their report, we've done all we can to address the problems they highlighted. The main ones are:

We, and almost all of agriculture in the UK and the rest of the world, use ammonium nitrate fertilisers. Ammonium nitrate is made using fossil fuels, it generates greenhouse gases and, a more recent worry, the vast bulk comes from Russia, so supplies are unreliable.

All cows, including ours, belch, which sounds like something to amuse schoolchildren who laugh at anything to do with burps. But actually, something so normal is causing damage to the atmosphere. The methane they burp is even more of a problem than carbon dioxide, because it's twenty-eight times as efficient at trapping heat and contributing to climate change. (There used to be a theory that cow farts were also responsible, which was even more amusing for schoolkids. In fact, although cows like all mammals do fart and there is small amount of gas released this way, it's the burps that make the largest methane contribution.) A fully grown cow can release up to 500 litres of methane a day, and across the world this amounts to

3.7 per cent of all greenhouse gases. That may sound like a small percentage – and it is compared to other offenders, but it is significant nonetheless. The Global Methane Pledge, which the UK is signed up to, aims to have methane reduced by 30 per cent by 2030.

Producing some of our animal feeds uses lots of energy, and they are often imported over long distances, another contributor to greenhouse gases. Soya and palm oil are particular culprits, with their production responsible for vast areas of deforestation in South America, which alone has been responsible for the loss of a land area as big as Spain since 2010. This loss of dense forest accounts for 12 per cent of greenhouse gas emissions. Although importing soya from deforested areas is illegal in the UK, it is very hard to police and one estimate is that about 30 per cent of our imports are coming from blighted rain forests.

On the plus side, our expert report showed that we were already doing some good things, and we are now doing a lot more. All the 'green' areas on the farm are doing sterling work sucking up carbon dioxide, the main greenhouse gas which accounts for over 70 per cent of all emissions. In a process known as photosynthesis, the plants suck it in, and with the energy from sunlight convert it into sugars which feed them, and in return they put out oxygen into the air. It's a really valuable job, and an important part of the fight against climate change.

The crops we are now growing on our pasture fields are doing their bit in this process of eliminating carbon.

By creating these herbal rich leys with mixtures of legumes, herbs, wildflowers and grasses, we are mopping up more carbon, as well as encouraging pollinators. The variety of plants improves the soil fertility by naturally adding nitrogen, they control weeds because there is no base ground, and they provide nutritious forage for our livestock. A wildflower that has really come back into its own in recent years is sainfoin: the name means 'healthy hay' in French. It was a fodder crop in previous centuries, it thrives on thin soil like ours, and is very popular with all the insect pollinators, as well as being a very attractive pink flower.

To feast on the pollen bonanza we have fifty beehives in the woods, and an observation hive for visitors to the Farm Park to watch these amazing creatures at work. The observation hive is set back from the viewing screen, so that visitors can watch but they can't tap on the hive or disturb the bees in any way. The hives belong to Chris Wells, of Cotswold Bees, and we play host to very popular courses he runs for anyone interested in beekeeping. Chris is a bee farmer (he is keen to stress he is not a bee keeper, because he runs a commercial business) and is based near Chipping Campden, about twelve miles from us, with other hives around the area. It started as a hobby for him, and in 2002 he went into business. Honey from our own bees, which love to feed on our sanfoin flowers, is a real treat, and if I'm around when Chris is there he might, if I'm lucky, give me a honey comb, which is the best honey ever. I spoon it on toast or stir it into my porridge for breakfast on a wintry morning – or for elevenses, afternoon tea, any excuse I can get.

When the wildflowers have gone over we harvest them, using a small combine harvester, and sell off the seeds, to keep the cycle going.

The bees also love the large field of sunflowers we plant every year, about 100,000 flowers, which give visitors to the Farm Park a wonderful place to visit for the eight weeks or so that they are in bloom, and for little children to get lost along the pathways. The birds, linnets and goldfinches in particular, feast on the seeds, and visitors at the right time of year can go home with a bunch of them. Like all yellow flowers, they symbolise happiness – and are the national flower of Ukraine, which seems particularly appropriate at this time. The sunflowers are particularly useful for the pollinators if we have a very hot summer, like 2022, when the wildflowers suffer from the drought.

As for fertiliser on our arable fields, some incredible technology has come to our aid. Instead of spreading indiscriminate amounts of fertiliser all over our crops, which was normal practice for many years, we now have a state-of-the-art system which means that messages from a satellite control our distribution of fertiliser. It started with more expert advice: we called in a firm of agronomists, scientific experts in soil and crop cultivation. They produced a map of our land, showing which parts were most in need of fertiliser, which needed only a little, and which needed none at all. As is the case everywhere, our soil varies – even in each field. The cab of our crop sprayer tractor was fitted with a satellite dish, and when the grid reference information from the agronomists was fed to the satellite, information received by the dish could remotely control the amount of fertiliser we were applying, varying it according to how much any particular bit of land needed it.

Mind boggling. I can't pretend to understand exactly how it works, but it's astonishing to watch the nozzles on the sprayer automatically switching off and on, or moderating the amounts of fertiliser. It was a big investment, but it has cut down our huge fertiliser bill and is altogether much better for the environment.

The system has greatly reduced the amount of ammonium nitrate we are using, and we are working on improving this more. We are now measuring the crop to see what the uptake of nitrogen is so that we can refine our spraying further.

We have also switched from using animal feed that includes soya, because it is so damaging to the rain forest. Some soya is grown in the UK, but the large majority of the soya that reaches our shores comes from South America. Much of it is used in human food manufacture, but over a third of the soya imported goes into animal feed. We are now using beans and barley which we grow ourselves, mixed with molasses from the British sugar beet industry and home-grown straw and silage, and our cattle and sheep live on this in the harsh winter months. We still buy some soya to include in the diets of our pigs and chickens, but we are working on eradicating it completely.

Animals like cattle, sheep and goats are ruminants, and they have multi-chamber stomachs to digest their food. Bacteria breaks down the cellulose in plant food, and the by-product is the methane released in burps, mentioned earlier. It's the work of these microbes, breaking down the cellulose, that creates methane, so we aim to take a lot of their workload off their stomachs by chopping up the fibres in the feed so that they can pass on more easily through the digestive chain.

We have a large Keenan feeder wagon that chops it up and mixes it, and we use another expert, a nutritionist, to tell us the right mix for our different breeds of animals. We can adapt the mix according to where they are in their life; in other words, ewes who are carrying or feeding lambs need more, so do cows with calves, so we use scales to measure exactly the right amounts for them all.

We use the same machine, which I call the Cake Mixer although it is more like a blender, to chop the fibres in the feed to the right size, which gives us quite a lot of control over the amount of methane the cows produce in their burps and is our next weapon in the fight against climate change.

Our 'catch crop', sown after our wheat harvest and before spring planting, gives the cattle and sheep turnips, radishes and rye to dine on. We strip graze, which means we move the animals across the fields using electric fences to prevent them trampling the whole crop. We always allow them access to grass to lie on when they are not feeding; I hate it when I see sheep eating fodder crops but with nowhere to go to get away from the muddy, churned-up ground.

As part of the *Countryfile* programmes we've looked at other future solutions, like replacing our gas-guzzling tractors and other heavy machinery with electric ones, but at the moment the technology falls short of being possible for large scale arable farms. We'll definitely keep it under review, because once the scientists have come up with feasible alternatives to diesel engines, it will be another step forward. Ultimately, our aim is to protect the planet and environment as much as we can, and we are constantly looking for ways we can help.

Every now and then, Duncan and I reflect on how far we've come from the days when we took over from Dad and Uncle John – from an environmental perspective and everything else. Back then we had 50,000 visitors a year to the Farm Park, and twenty staff. Today we have 180,000 visitors and employ more than 100 staff. From one shed for indoor attractions we now have four, and from a campsite that was just a field of grass with pitches for tents, we now have lodges, glamping, hard-standing for campervans and still some grassy pitches for anyone who prefers camping the old-fashioned way. We feel lucky, but we also know how hard we, and everyone who is employed here, has worked to get to where we are.

We can't see what's around the corner, and given what's happened just in the last few years, nothing is a certainty. But considering what we've managed to survive in the last twenty years, I am optimistic we have many good years – and Christmases – ahead of us.

Our Christmas routine nowadays is only slightly different from my childhood memories of the big day. My first job on Christmas morning, before anyone else is stirring, is to go down to the kitchen to put the enormous turkey into the Aga for five hours' cooking. We will have prepared it the night before, so all I have to do is pop it in. Then it's back upstairs with mugs of tea for Charlie and me while the children (well, adult children) pile on to our bed to open their stockings.

Some things never change, and the routine of feeding the animals in the winter months remains pretty much the same as in Dad's day. On any farm, regardless of the date on the calendar, the livestock come first. They don't know that it's a special day, and one of the most important things for animals is to have consistency, feeding them and inspecting them at the same time. It's vital to keep to their routine and there are no special Christmas 'treats' for them – treats for animals, whether they are farm animals or family pets, are not a good idea.

Instead of Dad's tractor and trailer, today we use a Kawasaki Mule, which has a three-person bench seat with a crate behind for the food and the sheepdogs.

Feeding starts in the main farmyard, where the pigs are in the looseboxes, the cows in the cattle sheds and assorted chickens running around the yard. Then we load up the mule and do a circuit of the fields, feeding the sheep, cattle and horses. It takes about two hours to get food to every creature on the farm and it's usually a two-man job, but at weekends one of us will do it. On Christmas Day, anyone who is around will join in, so that we all get as much time at home with our families.

The landscapes are so familiar to me and I love being out in the fields I remember from early childhood, when I was always eager to help out. I don't think I will ever lose the enthusiasm to get out there, whatever the weather.

Nowadays, I'm lucky enough to be able to take a break at Christmas, because we have excellent people working for us who are happy to take over the animal duties. The livestock manager, Mike Caunter, has done the rounds with the animals over Christmas for several years, and Luke New, another valuable member of our team, is also happy to join in, and did the duties last Christmas. Duncan lives in the nearby village of Kineton, where we have a few fields of sheep, and he will volunteer to check their welfare over the Christmas break.

The key to everyone having as much family time as possible over the festive season is to prepare in advance, by making sure all the feeders are topped up, the bedding is fresh, and there is plenty of clean water. Then it's a matter of praying there are no problems.

We don't have any animals, either on the farm or at the Cotswold Farm Park, who are giving birth at Christmas time, so it's a matter of a thorough check on them all, and if they are fit and healthy, you can get straight back home.

After a dog walk and breakfast comes presents. Then the feast, family packed in around the table. The food is traditional, much the same as Mum would have served. I'm in charge of the turkey – just thinking about that wonderful aroma when it comes out of the Aga, glistening and brown, makes my mouth water. Roast potatoes – who doesn't love them? Carrots, parsnips, sprouts, delicious stuffing and ladles of gravy. My favourite meal of the year. Afterwards we have our traditional dog walk, spreading bird seed along the field boundaries, and then we play games. We've relegated charades – Charlie never became a fan after her first terrifying ordeal. We play card games instead, and there's always lots of laughter and teasing.

As we get into bed at the end of the day, far too full and feeling contented, the house I've grown up in creaks like a human being breathing, the odd grumble in a pipe the equivalent of one of my snores. It's nice to think that in time, future generations will share the magic of this time of year on Bemborough Farm. I am always aware that I am lucky to be living here, in the countryside I love, carrying on with the work that my father started, and that other farmers undertook before us. Once my head is on the pillow, I concentrate my ears on the world outside, where the fields of our farm change throughout the seasons as they have done for centuries. Between the sighing of the beech tree branches, I find what I'm listening for: an owl's hoot. Now, to sleep.

I hope you, too, have a magical Christmas, reliving your own Christmas memories and dreaming of the many Christmases to come. From me, and every creature at Bemborough Farm and the Farm Park, Happy Christmas.

Adam Henson is the author of five books, including the *Sunday Times* bestseller *Like Farmer, Like Son* and the children's book *A Year on Adam's Farm*. Adam is perhaps the best-known farmer in the UK, presenting his own section on BBC's *Countryfile* to millions of viewers each Sunday evening. His other television credits include presenting *Lambing Live* alongside Kate Humble, *Secret Britain*, *Countryfile Summer Diaries*, *Big Wildlife Revival*, *Coast* and *Inside Out*. He has a monthly column in *Countryfile* magazine, as their resident farmer, as well as the *Cotswold Life* magazine. As well as his writing and television work, Adam runs Cotswold Farm Park in Gloucestershire, which pioneers rare breed conservation. His first book for Sphere, *Two for Joy*, was published in 2022.